The
Mountain

Nick Green

The Mountain
Copyright by Nick Green 2019
ISBN: 978-1-950613-07-6
Taylor and Seale Publishing LLC
3408 South Atlantic Avenue #139
Daytona Beach Shores, FL 32118

For Matthew

Shine on, you crazy diamond!

Prologue

When we are very young, we all have dreams of greatness—sometimes attainable and sometimes not. And because we are young, we have hope, and we have enjoyment in our dreams and in our hopes, sometimes without regard to the consequences of our actions—believing we are invincible. And these hopes and dreams lead us on to attempts of fulfillment.

Sometimes our attempts have unforeseen consequences, and sometimes we become discouraged with failure. But dreams are important. They are the impetus that leads us forward to risk, to try, to fall and try again. And sometimes the price seems too high. But if the dream is real, one will pick up and try again—without perhaps as much hope as before, but with determination and stubbornness against the voice that says "give up, already." And the dreamer sometimes will go against all odds and will lose his dream—and have to find something else to take its place. Only the individual decides which way to go, regardless of the price he has to pay. The dream may change shape, but he has to determine if it's worth the price to pay.

Nick Green's story reveals the heart of a youth who pays the price. He is on a mission—a journey which will change his life forever—no matter how it ends.

1

I had been out only a few weeks when I made the trip out east to visit T. The first sun peaked through the rolling mists shrouding the mountaintops. A light wind blew through the valley, cool and damp, rustling through the trees. Leaves floated to the ground, framed against the gray backdrop of the coming dawn. The hairs on my arm stood up. I shivered. I lit a cigarette and took a deep drag, leaning my head back against the wind to blow the smoke away from my eyes. We looked ahead, where in the dimness of the morning light we could just barely make out the faded sign posted at the trail head. It stared back at us, silent.

"It's freezing cold." I lit another cigarette, glancing upward at the endless sea of green that rose around us, half-hidden in the cold darkness of the early morning.

T glanced over at me. "It's five-thirty in the morning, bro. It's cold up here at night. I'm always cold."

I looked at him, my best friend of nearly thirty years, and smiled. "Cold or not, I'm glad you're here to do this with me. This would be miserable alone."

"Good thing I'm here then, huh?" He motioned toward the trail head. "Come on, let's go."

I lifted my backpack and slung it over my shoulder, feeling the weight of the strap pushing down heavily against my shoulder. We were outfitted lightly for what we had planned. We each carried our own supplies. My pack consisted of a couple of blankets, a few bags of beef jerky, an assortment of canned goods, two jugs of water, and our prize, a bottle of McAllen Eighteen Year. When we reached the peak, we would crack open the scotch and gaze down upon the world below us, victorious. We would be men, truly. We would be conquerors of nature. The endless hills and valleys would unfold, subservient beneath us. We would look upon them as gods among men, savoring our moment of triumph. We had assured ourselves we would find whatever it was we were looking for. I would find peace and freedom; I would find forgiveness. If only we could defeat The Mountain.

"Huh?" I snapped out of my dreamy reverie, putting pause to my dreams of glory. I glanced away from the mountains stretching above me. "You say something, T?"

He shook his head, pointing again toward the trail. "Let's get going. It's time." He took a few steps towards the old crooked sign marking the beginning of our journey, his feet plodding along the path. It was the path we knew would carry us to our destiny.

"Yeah. Yeah, okay, right." I stamped out my cigarette and followed him up the gentle incline into the trees. For half a moment, I hesitated, glancing back towards my car. My chest was tight. I breathed in deeply, tasting the flavor of the early morning mountain air, and then jogged forward, following after T, the sounds of my footsteps echoing into the trees.

The trail was easy at first, clear and well-marked. Cut logs ran along either side of the dirt path as it wound its way up through the foothills. It ascended slowly, running smooth and lazy beneath ancient trees. We trotted along in silence as squirrels ran along the side of the trail, occasionally, and then vanished into the trees. Unseen birds chirped around us. Alone on the trail, we had left civilization far behind us.

The sun began to vanish under the profusion of leaves, though it occasionally peeked back through from time to time, flashing into our eyes and then hiding again as quickly as it had come. Behind its' bright gaze, the mist swirled, rising like smoke above the trees. Then, our ultimate prize was still hidden from us, hiding unseen in the distance, wrapped in white. It was only a dream, then. It was only an idea, hiding from us high above the path. Beyond our sight it waited, beckoning.

We stopped for an early lunch at about eleven in the morning. We had no real way to tell what time it was, for we had brought no watches or phones. Time was no longer relevant. By the time I decided to stop, we were already feeling the strain of the trail, which had become almost imperceptibly steeper. My calves were burning with every step I took.

T and I sat on the ground, our backs leaning against the trees, treating ourselves to a meal of canned peaches and cold beans. As we sat on the side of the mountain under the comfortable shade, we appreciated the meal in a way that we never could have while sitting at a kitchen table. We were more than happy to rid ourselves of the weight of the cans on our backs.

It was something we hadn't considered; it would turn out to be one of many things we hadn't thought of, dashing off towards the mountain in the earliest hours of the morning, our heads swimming with the kind of dreams that every young man has when he prepares to fully exert his will against the ever-present oppression of the natural world, of Nature itself and all the world around him; to

3

fight the past and charge into the future; to enter the bush filled with trepidation and finally emerge as new men, victorious, reveling in the glory of our own souls, standing free upon the top of the world.

2

Only five or six days ago I'd made the decision to go see T. After everything that had happened down in Florida—all the misery and bull, the long nights and close calls, he went back to his old stomping grounds in North Carolina, and I'd been summoned out West to stay for a while somewhere where I could get over everything, get myself right, and try to put my life back together again.

All it had taken was a simple phone call, and there I was, heading east on I-10 in my beat up old Saturn, dreams of redemption dancing in my head. We would conquer The Mountain and reassert our place in the world. I liked the sound of it, so I tossed a few meager possessions in my back seat and took off. Visions of glory danced through my mind, sparkling, pure, and raw. This, this is how I would rewrite the story of my life. It would all begin again from here, from this journey.

A couple of hours into the drive, right as I hit the Louisiana border, I felt my stomach growling and pulled off into a truck stop to fill my car up with gas, and myself up with food. When I finished and went to buy a few packs of smokes for the road, I noticed bottles of liquor displayed prominently behind the counter—rows upon rows of them, from vodka to gin to bourbon—a veritable treasure trove of alcohol nestled next to cases of Camels and Marlboros.

I did a double-take. "You sell liquor here?"

The cashier looked at me as if I were a moron. "Yes. Right there behin' me." He paused, briefly. "Right ther' in front of yer face. *Sir*." He added the sir just to emphasize that he wasn't being rude, but only wondering if maybe I wasn't quite right if I couldn't see the display stretching out behind him.

"I mean, here, at a truck stop? I didn't think you could do that."

He laughed, suddenly, the noise bellowing out from deep inside and booming off the walls. He lifted a wrinkled hand to wipe spittle from his mustache, still chuckling. "Boy," he started. "This is Lee–see-anna. You can buy liquor just 'bout anywhere." His tone had changed sharply. He laughed again, without malice. "Was there somethin' in particular ya' had yer eye on?"

I ran my eyes along the selection, stopping for a little longer to examine the rows of whiskey bottles. They were well stocked. Eventually, my eyes landed on a bottle of Wild Turkey. It stared provocatively back at me. "Let's do a fifth of Turkey, yeah. That sounds pretty good about now."

He grinned. "Turkey it is. Cash or credit?"

I paid up and headed back out to the car, back onto the road, back to the same highway that stretched all the way across the southern United States. I pulled back into the lonely darkness. It wasn't more than fifteen minutes before I was glancing over at my newly purchased bottle. My intention had been to cruise on a while longer, a few more hours, then park at a rest stop somewhere and have a couple of sips of whiskey to help me get to sleep. It would leave me a nice, easy drive for the morning. That, of course, didn't quite work out.

I hadn't had a drink in months, due to my situation and where I'd been and all. But sitting there next to me, my lone silent traveling companion, the whiskey, looked more inviting than I'd expected. Like a good friend, it promised to help me pass the time, to drive on through to my destination with the radio blaring. The songs on the radio would sound better, the lyrics more poignant. The anticipation would become both greater and more tolerable. The miles would fly by, and I would be happily resting before I knew it. The bottle smiled at me, and I licked my lips and smiled back.

About halfway into the bottle, as I was careening down the highway, keeping it to a solid eighty-five, it occurred to me that I really shouldn't be drinking like this. After another song and a few more sips, I wasn't worried about whether or not I should be drinking. I lit another cigarette and rolled down the windows. I turned the radio up. Cruise on, cruise on, east and north, cruise on.

I'd woken up confused, the morning sun beating down on my face through the windshield. A rank smell permeated the inside of my car. The windows were up, and it was getting hot inside. I groaned, stretching out and trying to loosen up my legs. I fumbled with the window button, to no avail. "What the heck?" My mouth was miserably dry. I forced my eyes open, trying to take in my surroundings through the glare of the morning sun.

I grasped at the door handle, blindly pushing it open and stumbling out into the uncomfortably warm morning light. The sun seemed unbearably bright. I noticed, just then, the source of the smell: my shorts, as well as most of the driver's side of my car, were covered in vomit.

I lit a cigarette. It felt lousy, smoking with a dry mouth still tasting of liquor. I opted to finish my smoke

7

anyway, and then took another peek inside my car. My keys, along with the remaining third of the bottle of Turkey, sat in the passenger seat. I vomited again, quickly spinning around so that I was able to mostly miss coating the door of my car. The spin didn't sit well with my pounding head, and I threw up again.

From the looks of it, I was at a rest stop somewhere off of I-10. "Well, guess I can't handle my liquor anymore." And for good measure, I mumbled, "What the…" My voice sounded soft and sad. I hadn't had a drink in a few months, and this is what I chose to do? I felt like a moron; a miserably hungover, vomit-covered moron.

My mind still clouded by sleep and last night's whiskey, I headed across the parking lot to the bathroom. Standing in front of a sink with my head pounding and my stomach turning, I cleaned myself—and my shorts—as best I could. Leaning forward, I put my mouth under the faucet and drank for what seemed like several minutes. By that point, I didn't really care if anyone saw me or not. I splashed some water on my face and dried my hands before snatching a roll of paper towels and heading back towards my car. That, too, I cleaned up as best I could, ignoring the growing heat as the sun rose ever higher into the sky and reflected back at me off of the pavement. I changed my clothes right there in the parking lot, ignoring the offended stares of an elderly couple that had just pulled into the rest area. I tied my clothes up in an old grocery bag from my floorboard, sealing it up as best as I could manage. I thought about throwing it out, but instead tossed it into my trunk.

I sat down in the driver's seat and lit another cigarette. This one didn't taste quite so terrible. After rolling down my windows, I leaned back for a moment, sighing. I looked around me at the flat plains, dotted by the occasional lonely tree, and pulled deeply on my cigarette. The air around me, floating in through my open windows, was warm and dry. It smelled faintly of some unknown flower. Above me, I watched a string of billowing white clouds float over the sun, bathing the concrete below in shade.

For just one moment, my misery seemed to fade into the background as the clouds passed over me. I felt a sense of peace, brief but unmistakable. Slight setback aside, I was on my way…on my way to see T…on my way towards The Mountain. The chirping of birds was drowned out by the sound of my engine whirring to life.

Cigarette in hand, I pulled back out onto the highway and headed east toward the bright fire of the rising sun, a smile on my face.

3

I woke up under the shade of a tall tree, refreshed and renewed. The sun was high in the sky, its brightness assaulting the shade of the trail. "T!" I pulled myself to my feet, brushing the dirt off of my pants and back. "T?"

"Hey!" His head appeared between the trees. "How you feelin', brother?"

"Good." I smiled. "Actually good." I tried to gauge how much time had passed, but the foliage overhead made it nearly impossible to track the sun. "How long was I asleep?"

"Dunno. Couple hours."

"You get a nap in?"

"Nah, brother, I'm already getting plenty of sleep these days."

I took a few steps, bending my knees and stretching my stiff legs. I breathed deeply, smelling the forest and the blooming flowers strong in my nose. I exhaled. I lit a cigarette. "You 'bout ready to get goin', or what?"

"Well," T strolled over closer to me, so I could hear him clearly above the buzzing of the forest. "I was thinkin', maybe we ought'a plan things out a bit. Figure when we wanna sleep, when we wanna eat. Which peak, exactly, to go for. Ya' know, all that jumk before we get to the fun part."

"Yeah," I replied. "That sounds good, buddy." I felt sad, suddenly, and lost, as I watched T walking between the trees. I felt strangely alone, there in the company of the best friend I'd ever had.

Despite our constant assertion that we were brothers —and in my mind, we were—we had been born cousins, just about a month apart. We had lived, growing up, just a few houses down from each other. We had played on the same baseball and football teams. We hung out at the same malls and chased the same groups of girls. We'd had our first beer together and smoked our first joint together. He was the first friend I ever had—the best friend I ever had.

My first clear memory was T and me hanging on a grassy hill, enjoying a warm Tennessee spring. The sun was shining in a clear blue sky. The azure landscape of the heavens stretched above us. We were free and uninhibited, running and laughing, smiling like only children can. We spent hours in the field, doing nothing in particular. We played tag and imitated our favorite super-heroes. We talked about our favorite television shows, acting them out along with a thousand imaginary friends. We made up our own games, whose rules only we knew, and whiled away the days playing them endlessly.

The spring melted into summer, and on into endless years of youth. Time felt as if it didn't move, back in those days. Every romance was to be forever. Every victory was utter and complete. The days in front of us were endless. Spring would always come again, with its promise of new things, and then on to another everlasting summer. There was always another baseball season or another birthday party; there was nothing ahead but promise and great things, sunshine and warm water.

Our laughter was eternal. Our smiles were endless. Our hearts were filled with freedom and love. Our souls were light and boundless. Existence itself was joy, back then, in the summers of our youth. We needed nothing else. We needed no reason to be happy, save that we existed and were there to enjoy the splendors of the world. It was all there for the taking, and we could take and take with no measure of greed, for the well was bottomless. We had only to want and the world was ours.

I felt the sadness, like a blue blanket, wrap around me again. Those times were long past. We were adults now, with jobs and bills, obligations and addictions. We'd known heartache and pain. We'd lost friends and family. We'd seen the best and worst of people. That innate happiness, that carefree joy, had faded into obscurity. It felt somehow wrong, feeling such a sudden sense of inescapable loss while out experiencing the abundant glory of Nature with my best friend by my side. I glanced over at T. "I'm glad you're here, buddy. I couldn't do this without you."

He gave me a funny look, scrunching his faces and squinting his eyes. "I've always got your back, man. Always have, always will. You know that."

I smiled a sad smile. "Yeah, T. I know. I got yours, too, my friend." My chest felt hollow and empty. "Hey, T. Thank you. Ya' know, for always havin' my back and all."

"Of course, brother. Always."

I forced the sadness from my mind, as best as I could manage. "So," I started. "We still need to figure out just where the hell we're goin'. We don't wanna just wander in circles until we're out of food, ya' know?"

"Yeah. I been thinkin' 'bout that'n, too."

I grinned at him. "That came out country, buddy. Been thinkin' 'bout that'n, have ya?"

He laughed. "I guess that's the Nash-vulle in me." He emphasized the second syllable of Nashville, dropping into that long, soft u sound that we'd always heard growing up. "But yeah, you're right, man. You got any ideas on it?"

I shrugged. "I've been glancin' over some maps and stuff, but I'm not all that picky about which peak. As long as we're on top of Grandfather, I'm a happy man." I paused. "But I've been thinkin' you wanna have a go at Attic Window?"

"That didn't end well last time."

"Yeah, and I'll be damned if I'm going to let that peak beat us! Besides, last time we were seventeen and brought two bottles of water each and tried to do it in a single day."

He laughed, deep and loud. It resonated throughout the forest, echoing ghost-like through the trees. "That was some scenario, wasn't it?"

"Yeah," I laughed. "The folly of youth, eh?"

"I don't know about you, my friend, but I plan to be young forever."

"Of course you do." I looked at him, remembering our attempt at the peak over a decade before. We had come stumbling off the trail, exhausted and dehydrated, barely having reached the halfway point. This time would be different. This time had to be different.

"So, Attic Window, one more time?"

"Yeah," I answered. "Attic Window, one last time."

The Ranch 4

I often reminisced about the previous attempt when I had arrived at The Ranch a week or so after things had gone bad in Florida. The enormity of everything that happened hadn't settled in yet, and I was just thrilled to be somewhere with clean beds and hot meals. The place itself wasn't anything overly impressive, at first glance. The main facility was a house positioned at the highest point of a few acres of land in the Texas hill country. There was a smaller building consisting of a kitchen and a few small offices about twenty yards away, on the other side of the hilltop. Between them was a pool that would prove far too cold to enjoy in the fall weather. At the bottom of the hill was a larger structure—which I would soon learn was called the barn—where all of us who'd gotten ourselves into this same predicament would meet for various lessons a few times a day. Sundays, too—no exceptions.

The shuttle was an old white van that dropped me off right in front of the offices. I was sweating when they dropped me off and led me over to talk to the doctor. A group of unfamiliar faces, sitting at a picnic table a few feet away and smoking cigarettes, stared at me as I walked into the building with my head down. I didn't have any idea what the hell they thought of me, walking in ragged with my uncombed long hair covering half my face, but in my own mind I'm sure it wasn't good. I was sure they all knew just what I was, and what I'd done.

14

I don't remember much of the next few hours. I was cold and my muscles were aching. The staff went through my bags, and a doctor asked me a million and a half questions that I didn't feel at all like answering. None of them were anything less than kind to me, but I was convinced that I knew what they thought. "Are you okay?" wasn't a question, but a judgment. They were all okay, and here I was the object of their scornful pity.

The whole process went by quick enough. They confirmed that neither was I in imminent danger of dying, nor trying to smuggle in a pile of drugs and weapons, and eventually led me to a small room with two double beds where I was allowed to unpack my bag and relax until dinner. The other bed was unoccupied, I was informed, allowing me the luxury of my own room —at least for a few days. I chose the left side of the room and settled in. For an hour or two, I did nothing. No one came by. I didn't read any of the stack of books I'd brought along with me, or any from the small closet that had been dubbed a "library" located a few doors down.

Instead, I just sat and stared blankly at the wall. I don't remember what I thought about, or what memories climbed into my consciousness. I only remember that I wanted to be sad. I had to be sad, but instead I felt absolutely nothing. I was empty inside. I sat in silence and pretended that the world didn't exist. I pretended that nothing at all had happened. Nothing had ever happened. All of creation was simply me alone in this room. Two twin beds, two dressers, two laundry baskets, and a lamp. These items comprised all of creation. There was nothing more, and nothing less.

At some point, my door opened every so slightly, and a pretty girl with dark hair peeked in. I could tell she worked there. "Are you okay?"

"Yeah."

"Dinner's going to be ready soon."

"Not hungry."

"You should eat. It'll make you feel better to eat. And then, after, the doctor wants to see you again."

"Not hungry," I repeated. "Just tell me when I have to see the doctor."

I could feel the pity pouring from her eyes. "You know it is going to get better, right?" There was no hint of anything but kindness in her voice, but I was sure that, somewhere beneath that facade, there was nothing but judgment.

I stared down at the floor and shook my head. I said nothing.

"Dinner's at six. The doctor wants to see you at seven." I heard the door close. A few seconds later, it opened again, just an inch or two. "I promise you, it will get better. Do you want a cup of coffee or something? We have snacks. Water. Tea. Really, there's a lot out here. if you want, I can show you where-"

"Coffee," I said, resisting my urge to simply lie down and cover my head with a pillow. "Please. Coffee would be nice, please."

"Sure," she said. "Cream? Sugar?"

"Black. Black is fine. Don't go to any extra trouble, not for me."

"Don't worry about that." She pushed the door open a little wider. I could see her face, again. She gave a small half smile. "Just let me know what you need."

16

"Really. Black is fine." I relented, and let my voice soften. "Thank you."

"Of course." She disappeared, shutting the door behind her. A few minutes later, I heard a light knock.

"Yeah?"

"I have your coffee." The door pushed open, just a few inches. "Is it okay if I come in?"

"Does it matter if I say no?"

"Of course," she said. "I'm not a doctor. Unless I'm pretty sure you're trying to tie your shoestrings from your neck to the ceiling fan, I'm not going to barge in."

"Come in, sure." I stood up. I still looked disheveled. I hadn't changed clothes in days, and my hair was a tangled mess that would've made a bird's nest look ornate and orderly.

She took a single step inside, and stretched out her arm, offering me the coffee. "We just made a brand new pot."

"Who the hell brews a pot of coffee at night?" I scoffed, accepting the mug regardless.

"We made it for you."

I'm not sure why, but that single simple statement left tears welling up in my eyes. I knew it was no big deal —that it was her job. Either way, logic could offer no resistance as the rush of sudden emotion pounded against the floodgates. I managed a meek, "thank you."

She nodded. "Dinner at six, okay? You need to eat. It'll make you feel better."

I sighed. "Okay, yeah, dinner at six."

"It's just across the yard, in the little building where the doctors office is. Do you want me to remind you before?"

"Please," I said. "I would really, truly appreciate that. I think I just need to lie down for a while first, and without my phone, I have no damn idea what time it is."

"I'll knock on your door about fifteen minutes before, to give you a little time to prepare." She started to shut the door, but paused for just a moment. "I mean it when I said things will get better. They will. But you have to believe, too. You have to help make them better. I promise you, though, I'm not lying. Do you believe me?"

I took a sip of my coffee, staring again at the blank wall on the other side of the room. "I'll be ready for dinner by a quarter to six," I said. Without a word, she closed the door to the room.

These had been bad days. This time was going to be different.

5

With our minds made up, we shouldered our packs and took off down the trail. By now, the sun was high overhead. Beams of light shone through the cracks in the foliage, shining rays of sunlight dotting our path. The cool morning had long vanished into afternoon heat. Mixed with the moisture rising off of the trees, the air had become humid and thick. It was only the steady, soft breeze blowing through the trees that kept the hike tolerable.

I stopped to catch my breath, wiping a bead of sweat off my forehead. I held one of my water jugs high, dumping it down my throat and allowing some to dribble down my chin and onto the front of my sweat-stained shirt. The water was warm, by now, but it still felt wonderful. "How you holdin' up, T?"

"It's hot, brother."

"You're tellin' me, man. I swear, this was easier ten years ago."

"You were probably twenty pounds lighter ten years ago."

"You're one to talk, T." I laughed and took another long gulp of water.

"Harsh."

"Hey, there are worse things in life than being old and fat," I joked.

"I told you, bro, I'll never be old." T was some fifteen yards behind me, stopped to examine a colorful plant growing along the trail side. He leaned forward, breathing in the aroma of the flower. "I'm good, though, always good."

"Yeah, not tiring out yet?"

"Nah, man. I don't get tired."

"Yeah, okay." I shook my head and stuck the water jug back in its place at the side of my pack.

"Believe it!" He jogged ahead to catch up while I stopped to wait. "Young forever, just like I said."

"Ya' know, T," I said. "It really is beautiful out here. All joking aside, I'm so darn glad we're out here doing this. I needed this."

He smiled that big wide smile of his that seemed to take up his whole face. He patted me on the shoulder. "One last crack at the mountain, my friend. Before you're too old to handle it."

"Before I'm too old?" I laughed. "So that's how it is, huh?" We started walking again.

"I keep tellin' you, brother, I'll never get old." His grin widened and he sort of leaned over, playfully knocking his pack into mine. "It'll just be you, an old man, whining and moaning and sitting on your butt all day. Doing... I dunno, drinkin' whiskey and playing backgammon or some other board games. You'll be old and decrepit, and I'll always stay young. "

"Backgammon, that's the best you got?"

"Hey, I dunno. Pick whatever old person game you want," he said. "You know what I mean."

"Yeah, T." I got quiet, then, looking over at my old friend marching steadily along the trail with his head held high and a look of unadulterated joy upon his face. I imagined being an old man, frail and weak, and him still the same, frozen in time. It made me sad as hell, the thought of getting old alone.

I remembered our good times before our first attempt at the mountain.

I'd split with my wife about a year earlier. I wasn't handling it well and had hit the bottle hard. Anything I could find to numb the pain went into my body. I remembered calling T, late at night, lost in a haze of whiskey and painkillers. "I'm just not okay," I remembered saying.

"You'll always be okay," he told me. "'Cause you got friends who got your back, who'll make sure you're okay."

Somewhere in the middle of my intoxicated, half-coherent ramblings, I mentioned a job offer I had way down in South Florida. I was only half serious about it, the idea of just dropping it all and running down to sunny Florida to take a new job, start a new life.

"You should take it," he'd said.

I'd been hesitant. "I dunno, man. I'm not sure I wanna just up and move halfway across the country alone. Florida's a long way down there."

"So don't do it alone," he'd said. "Pick me up on the way. Hell, North Carolina can't be that far out of the way. We'll get a two bedroom on the beach and live it up!"

"You serious?"

"Hell yeah, brother. Can't have you down there all alone, drinking your sadness away the way you do. And besides," he'd laughed. "South Florida doesn't exactly sound like a terrible place to live or anything."

I'd picked him up a few days later in a half full U-Haul, and we did just what we said: we rented a cool little two bedroom, right there on the beach. The weather was gorgeous, the women were beautiful, and the seafood was fresh. The drinks were always cold and our glasses were never empty for long. We were two young bachelors having the time of our lives, living every day as if we were on vacation. Before long, I was even showing up to work wearing sandals and a Hawaiian shirt. We really had a great time, until all the miserable stuff went down and I had to go back out west to put myself back together.

"You all right back there, brother?" He called out from some fifty yards ahead of me. "You're slowin' down on me."

I snapped out of my haze, pushing the memories aside and jogging ahead to catch up. "I'm good, T! Just lost in thought, ya' know?"

He waited for me to catch up, as I'd done for him a few moments earlier. "There's a little stream about a mile ahead. It's been raining like hell up here lately, so hopefully the water isn't too high."

"I can't imagine one of these little mountain streams swelling up too much." We would soon find out just how wrong I was. The mountain was old and proud; it would not willingly submit to our whims, full of hubris as we were.

The sound of the stream flowing over the rocks soon reached our ears, far sooner than expected. As we drew closer, its roar rose up and filled our ears. By the time we were coming around the final bend before the water came into view, the noise of the rushing rapids was so loud that we were nearly shouting to be heard over it.

"T!" I yelled. "Is my memory gone crazy, or was this a tiny little creek last time we were here?"

"That's what I remembered, too, brother. But like I said, we been gettin' a whole lot of rain recently."

We had, indeed, underestimated just how much the rain had affected the creek. It was a raging river, at least eight or ten feet across, cascading furiously down the mountainside. Caps of white jumped over the rocks, slamming down into the water, spraying foamy droplets high up into the air.

"Hell." I stared at the water, my heart sinking. My dreams of salvation were washed down the river, petering out and dying in some cold, unknown pool far below.

"Well, hell indeed, my friend." T leaned close to the water. It splashed up, spraying his face. "That water is fast. Fast and cold."

My heart fell lower; the weight of the pack on my back grew heavier; the weight of the world fell upon my shoulders. I sank to my knees, tasting the bitterness of failure on my tongue. Dreams of the peak danced in front my eyes, falling apart as I reached out for them.

"How we gonna cross this?" T sat down next to me, laying a comforting hand on my shoulder.

"Cross this?" I looked at him. "You're really crazy, T. This isn't a little creek like before. We'll die trying to cross this thing. I'm not exaggerating, we'll die. I'm not fooling around here."

"Nah, brother. No way." He lifted his hand and clapped me on the shoulder. "Let's get some logs, lay them across, and push them between those rocks sticking up. It'll take a bit, but hell, what else're we gonna do, right?"

I glanced upwards, shaking my head.

"Right?" He was already scanning the surrounding woods for suitable logs. "Come on. We have a mission, my friend, and failure is not an option." He slapped me hard on the back, almost jovially. "Time to get to it! Right?"

"Right."

We did just as he suggested. It was an arduous process, sweaty and exhausting. It made me miss the chilly temperatures of the early morning. For at least an hour we were going back and forth, into and out of the forest, dragging logs along the ground. Eventually, we had some semblance of a bridge stretched across the water.

"This," I commented. "Is the kind of work that calls for a cold beer."

"Hell no, man. You put a beer in my hand and tell me to drag these logs, I'm giving up five minutes into it. No."

"You tell me to do this any other day, beer or not, and I'm giving up five minutes into it."

"You're telling me, brother."

I pushed my boot against one of the logs. It held firm. I stared uncertainly at our work. "You think it'll hold?"

"Probably."

"Probably? Probably gets us killed, bro."

"It'll hold."

"You sure?"

"Sure enough."

"How sure is sure enough? If you're not one hundred percent certain, then let's rethink this."

"It'll hold."

I frowned at T.

He looked back at me, a grin spread across his face. There was no hint of fear in his eyes. "I'll go first, okay? That enough certainty for ya'?"

"Well, not really, but... ." I motioned with my hands. "Have at it." A pause. "And please, be extra careful."

"Yeah, of course."

24

"I mean it, T."

"I know." He stepped forward, cautiously stretching out one foot to test the closest log. Satisfied with the way it felt, he shifted his weight, leaning forward and gingerly putting one foot in front of the other. With tepid steps, one at a time, inch by inch, he crossed the raging waters. Standing on the opposite bank, he turned to face me with a huge grin stretched wide across his face. "Nothin' to it, my brother."

Still unsure, I stepped forward onto our makeshift bridge. The first log held firm. I stepped onto the second, and then the third. I felt it roll beneath my feet. I shot my arms out to the side, steadying myself. The log shifted again and I lurched left, then hard to the right. I regained my balance, momentarily, and then I was suddenly tumbling sideways. My arms flailed outwards, but they found only empty air.

The first sensation I felt was the icy water entering my lungs. My body slammed against the logs. I sank down, fast and hard, my vision disappearing into the rapids. For a moment, the pale visage of death stared directly into my eyes, and all I could do was stare hopelessly back. Even as my feet impacted the rocky creek bed, I was stiff, my body wracked with a freezing fear. The water rushed past me, pulling me deeper, holding my head beneath its icy grip. I floundered, helpless, unable to pull my head above the rapids.

And then, by some instinct deeper than consciousness, my feet pushed hard against the rocky surface, my hands stretching upward. I managed to grab the log with one hand, and then the other. I pulled with all my might, even as my vision began to tunnel and fade away. The cold was deep, so deep in my body that it felt like an icy rope was tightening around my insides. With one last effort, my head burst out of the water, and then I was struggling up the log. My arms felt as if they were pulling from my sockets as I struggled. And then, finally, I was on top of the log, lying on my stomach and gasping for air. My lungs burned. My body was numb.

Hand over hand, inch by inch, I dragged myself along the makeshift bridge and onto the bank. I was cold, wet, and exhausted, coughing and swearing, but very much alive. I felt the cold fingers of death receding from my throat as I lay gasping in the grass, my clothes soaked through to the bone. I could vaguely make out the sound of a shouting voice.

"Hey!" T was leaning over me. "Hey, man, I thought that was it! You okay?"

I continued gasping for air, still struggling to regain my breath. I could still feel the cold of the water deep inside my body.

"Hey!" T kneeled down, unsure of what to do. "Hey, man, are you okay?"

"I'll be fine." I was barely able to choke the words out. I coughed, cold water and spit running down my chin. Panic overtook me once again. "My pack! My pack!"

"Don't worry," T said, just the vaguest hint of a smile forming at the corner of his lips. "The thing's still attached to your back."

I breathed a sigh of relief. My breathing finally began to slow down. "Wow." Lying there, soaking wet and cold, I couldn't think of anything else to say. "Wow." I wasn't quite sure how long I lay there for as the heat of the afternoon sun struggled to penetrate my soaked-through clothes.

"Can you get up?"

My eyes were closed, and my wet hair was plastered to my face. I nodded an affirmative.

"Come on, brother. There's a nice sunny spot up ahead, just fifty yards or so. Let's get you into some dry clothes, and then we'll set up camp and see if we can salvage anything out of your pack. We've gone far enough today."

I forced a smile. "Works for me, T."

6

As luck would have it, we were able to salvage almost everything in my pack. T wandered off among the trees to collect firewood before dark. Shirtless and wearing a borrowed pair of shorts, I took to hanging my own clothes to dry on the surrounding tree limbs. My body was dry, finally, and I was as comfortable as I could reasonably expect to be.

Most of my pack, luckily, was salvageable. The clothes and blankets were soaked, but would be dry by morning. The food and first-aid kit had remained sealed. One of my water jugs had torn free and been lost to the river, but the other, despite some battering, hadn't sprung any leaks. We'd each carried a map before. Now, we had only one. My gear was waterlogged, but I imagined most of it would still function.

The sun hung low in the western sky, huge and gold, exploding in a final splendor before its time came to retreat beneath the hills and abandon the world to darkness once again. The mists surrounding the distant peaks seemed to thicken, engulfing the mountains as the surrounding world shrunk, leaving only me and my wet clothes on the branches and the outline of a tent against the trees wrapped in a circle of twilight.

In that moment, the world was small, and I alone walked upon it. The only things that ever had or ever would exist were there in that small clearing, clinging to the last vestiges of a fading light. I felt so huge and so alone, wordlessly meandering back and forth. The tents were pitched, the food—minus dinner—was wrapped in a bag and hanging from a tree, and there I sat upon a rotting log, pondering the smallness of my own meager existence.

The endless miles I'd traveled turned over in my head. Everything that had led me to this moment condensed into a tiny point and suddenly exploded outward, a cosmic big bang within my own mind. I could've been sitting there for years, for all I knew, when the sound of snapping twigs forced me back to the present.

T came crashing through the trees, his arms piled high with firewood. "We're good to go, bro. There was plenty of dry wood right here within twenty feet or so of the campsite. How great is that?"

"Yeah." Now dry, I grabbed a hanging shirt and pulled it over my head. I set to work on the fire. It was no time at all before it was tall and bright, shining like a blazing beacon in the darkness. The flames stretched upwards towards the heavens. High above us, the peak had disappeared into the night sky. Even unseen, we could feel its presence beckoning to us, challenging us. It didn't dare mock us. Hidden beneath the blanket of the night, it called to us, its siren song wailing high, echoing off the mountains the through the silent valleys below.

We ate dinner in a contemplative silence while our fire kept the ever present darkness at bay. Not long after we finished eating, T gave me a short nod and wandered off toward his tent. I sat for a while longer, watching the fire dancing against the backdrop of the night sky. Sleep tugged at my eyelids, and I soon found myself drifting off into a restless sleep.

7

The stars were shining high and bright in the South Florida sky. Piercing flashes of white and red reflected off of the still palm trees. Silence, dark and heavy and sad, so thick it was choking, filled the air. Everything was blurry, clothed in shadow. Vague, irregular shapes danced beyond my vision, coming and going rapidly, then slowly, before disappearing into the ground and falling back from the sky.

I was crying, screaming. My tears pooled on the ground, rising higher until my head was barely above the water. Shapes swam beneath my feet, vicious shapes that threatened to consume me and tear my very soul into a thousand pieces. My heart beat high above my head, faster and faster, ready to explode at any moment. The shapes watched me, unblinking, unrelenting. They circled. My screaming continued, but no sound emanated from my lips. The silence and darkness grew smaller, pulling the formless shapes ever closer. They snapped at my toes, violently thrashing beneath the impenetrably dark water.

Sound exploded, suddenly, back into my world. The lake of tears rushed away with a raucous crash. Wailing sirens filled the air. T was lying on the ground, still and cold, dressed in a suit of old bones. His eyes were closed. His skin was pale. The shapes still crawled beneath the darkness, and they were coming for him.

The monsters were closing in. I could feel them. They lurked in the bushes and beneath derelict cars, glaring at me with beady red eyes, gnashing row upon row of razor sharp teeth. They were coming. Vicious and hateful, they were coming. Like wraiths, they were coming. Death gazed down upon us, laughing.

The sky split open with a thunderous roar as the world crumbled to pieces around me. The suffocating darkness gave way to bright artificial lights. They were colder, somehow, than the night had been. White walls and men in white coats surrounded me. The world was sterile. I was running, I was sure, down a hallway that never changed, passed a hundred doors that all looked the same. My feet never touched the ground, and I couldn't be sure if I was moving, but I was running all the same.

"Where the hell is T?" My voice didn't work, but the words echoed in my head.

"I'll always be with you, brother." It resonated in my mind, his words coming to me from a formless void as the walls tumbled down around me. The lights exploded into brightness and then burnt out, the white of the world fading away to formless black.

There was only darkness. Empty, lonely darkness. The infinite void so close around me as it stretched forever on into miserable eternity.

Only me, alone.

Me, alone.

Everything is empty.

I am infinity. I am emptiness. I am the eternal void. Now I am become Death, Destroyer of Worlds.

The endless emptiness tore itself away, leaving me standing alone in a parking lot, staring up at an empty sky. The stars had long since died away. The streetlights were dark.

The faint sound of sirens faded away into the distance. The silence of the eternal void wrapped itself around the night.

Just me, standing in a parking lot, tears streaming down my face. My soul is the lonely night, consumed by the emptiness of all humanity, pervaded by every tear that ever had or ever would be shed. The eternal sadness of the human condition sat upon my shoulders, and I crumbled under its weight.

Me alone, standing in an empty parking lot.

Me alone, for all of endless time, floating formless in the void.

Just me.

Me alone.

Me alone in the empty night, waiting under a blank, starless sky for forgiveness that could never come.

Salvation rode away into the void, and I stood watching, alone in the empty parking lot where time stood still, meaningless and small.

Under the empty sky I cried, cried unending tears for all life lost to the all-consuming void, to the boundless ends of human cruelty, to the eternal emptiness of a billion lost souls, silent in the endless night.

Empty and alone, I cried for my brother. And for myself, only the silence without shape was left to quiet my lost soul, standing always in the darkness of the timeless void.

8

I opened my eyes, still in a fog, and peeled open the flaps of my tent. The sun was still hidden behind distant peaks. The horizon had only just began to glow with the first light tendrils of dawn, reaching upwards to grasp at the retreating darkness of the night sky. Mists rose off of the mountains, the fuming breath of some long forgotten God. It swirled around the peaks and sunk into unseen valleys, hiding their secrets beneath a soft wave of white.

The air was cold and damp. I shivered, making my way barefoot across the clearing towards my pack. My boots, hanging by the laces from a tree high above the still smoking embers of our fire, were smoke-dried and warm against my feet as I pulled them down and laced them up. "Bring on the brightness!" My voice echoed against the cliffs.

"What's that, brother?" T was seated at the edge of the clearing.

"I said, bring on the brightness! It's a new day. Hopefully, it's the kind of day that doesn't involve another goldarn swim in a freezing river." I smiled, ignoring the vague unsettling feeling that my dream had left me with. "How 'bout you, T? You good?"

He returned my smile, but something about his face was inexplicably sad. "Always, man. You know I'm always good, now."

"The hell's that mean, anyways?"

T shook his head. "You know you don't need to worry about me." He walked over and laid a hand on my shoulder. "I mean it, really. No pain, no reason to complain." He squeezed my shoulder. "For real, you gotta' quit worryin' about me."

"Okay, buddy." I nodded my head at him. "Okay."

"What about you? I mean... not just know, ya' know." He turned away, focusing his eyes on the horizon. "I mean, after everything went down in Florida and all. I know that wasn't easy on you, being left behind and all."

"I'm... ya' know, T, today I'm okay. One day at a time, right?"

"One day at a time, huh? That one of the things they taught ya' at wherever the hell it was you got yourself sent off to?"

"Somethin' like that."

"It actually workin' for ya'? The garbage they taught ya', I mean. All of it."

"Yeah," I said. "Well enough so far, at least. Some of it, ya' know..." I shook my head, looking down on my feet. "Some of it just feels like it'll never go away. It's rough, man, after all the years, all the sh--. It's been a long time since everything was... I dunno, normal? Since I was really normal."

"Brother, brother," he responded. "You're as normal as any of us. Heck, probably more normal. The way we live today, man, it's not natural, ya' know? I dunno, it seems like being okay with all of that, that would be not normal. We weren't meant to live like this, my friend. This rush-rush, compete-compete, compare yourself to everyone else up and down the street... It's not the way we're wired."

"Natural or not, everybody else seems to find a way to deal with it. Without, ya' know, pulling the sort of stuff I pulled."

"Hey, everyone goes through a rough patch, ya' know?"

"That's underselling it just a bit, don't ya' think?" I laughed. "Just a rough patch, that what we're callin' it now?"

"Brother," T answered. "We can call it whatever the hell you want. What matters is that you're here now. You're you again, and you're gonna stand on top of this mountain and piss down on your own demons."

"Thanks, T." I smiled. "I mean it, thank you."

"Just… Man, ya' gotta tell me when stuff's got ya' like that. Ya' gotta tell me when you need help. You know I'm here, man. Even after everything, you know I'm always with you."

"I know, T. Thanks."

"No need, my friend." He hesitated. "You really think this is it, brother? With everything, I mean?"

"I do."

"Don't lie to me."

"It's done, T. I'm done. There was so much more to it than I ever knew, ya' know? I learned a lot, out there, about where it all comes from and what's going on deep down in my mind and all that sorta' shit."

"It helped? Like, really, deep down, helped?"

"It did," I said. "I mean, there's no instant fix, ya' know? But it helped, it did. I wouldn't say the past few weeks have been easy… Hell, I'm here though, right?"

"Yeah, brother. I'm glad to hear it. I mean, you look good. You sound good. I just wanted to make sure that you weren't just fakin' it for me, ya' know? So I wouldn't worry and all." He looked me right in the eyes. "If you need to talk, you know I'm here, right? I'm always here, brother, if you need me."

"Thanks, T."

"Yeah, man. Yeah."

We fell into silence, lost in our own heads. We watched as the sun continued its ascent. The dew vanished as it climbed ever higher and the first hint of warmth crept into the wind. Without a word, we set to repacking our camp. Minutes later, we were on our way, the path beneath our feet growing steeper with each step.

T's voice broke through the silence. "I was thinkin', man. We don't have to rush this. What would be nice is if we took an extra day or so, right, and planned it so that we spend the night right there before we hit the peak. That way, we can wake up early and get goin' as soon as it starts to get light. Hit the peak and catch the sunrise! How great does that sound?"

"That sounds like a helluva plan, my friend."

"Right?" He said. "And going back down should be easier and quicker, so we should still be solid on food and water, especially if we refill our jugs at that last stream. We've got those purification tabs, now, so it won't be like last time."

"I sure hope not. That was real miserable."

"Yeah," T agreed. "I think we'll be all right. I'm not down for a repeat of last time, either."

9

Twelve years earlier was the first time climbing the mountain had occurred to us. We were seventeen years old. Fighting through boredom and a healthy dose of teen angst, we were determined to find a way to drink away our spring break. Turned away by every liquor store in town, we finally acted on the advice of a clerk, who didn't look to be much over the legal drinking age himself: "Why don't you guys do what everyone else your age does and just pay some old homeless dude to score ya' some booze?"

His lack of tact aside, the advice proved fruitful. Three days into our break, there we stood with a handle of cheap whiskey and no idea where to drink it.

After some deliberation, we found ourselves sitting under the shade of a tall oak tree in the nearest park, passing back and forth a bottle while we enjoyed the cool breeze blowing in off of the mountains.

"So what the … ya' wanna do?" T took a swig and handed me the bottle.

"Dunno." I gulped down the whiskey.

"We should do somethin'."

"Yeah, prolly should."

"I mean, we should do somethin' new. Somethin' b.a.a.a.a.d."

"Like what?" I passed the bottle back to him.

"Let's go to Alaska! Live off the land, ya' know?"

"You're crazy."

He took another sip and shot me a frustrated look. "I'm serious, brother. We could pull it off. We could do it."

"Bro, I..."

"No," he interrupted. "I've thought about it. I mean, I've really thought about it. It's totally dratted possible. C'mon, think about it! Us versus nature, brother! We get up there, man, and just live off the land for a while. We could do it."

I shook my head and took another swig from the bottle.

"You don't think we could?"

"It's not that," I said.

"What, then?"

I laughed.

"I'm serious, what?"

"Bro, we're halfway through a week-long break. That's a long trip, not some drop-and-go-for-a-few-days kinda thing."

"Yeah," he agreed, sounding disappointed. "We could do it, though. Someday, I mean."

"Yeah," I said. "Yeah, T, we could. Sounds like a pretty great adventure to me."

He smiled. "Hell yeah, brother. Someday."

"Someday." I meant it, too. At least, I thought I did. I didn't know, then, what the future would hold. At seventeen, the idea of growing old and having dreams pass me by was as foreign and unreal as going off to war or getting married. Concepts, only, and nothing more. I couldn't have known we'd never have the chance to make that trip.

"Well, then." T stood up. He wobbled on his feet, reaching out to steady himself against our shade tree. He grabbed the whiskey from my outstretched hand and helped himself to another drink. "What the heck we gonna do with the next couple a' days?"

I took the bottle. "Drink?"

"Nah," he said. "Nah, man, there's gotta be something better to do. I want a real adventure!"

"Something better to do while we drink?" I laughed.

"Fair enough."

"Well, I offered the drinkin' part. Rest is all you, buddy."

We both laughed, continuing to pass the liquor back and forth. Even to the greatest of optimists, it would've been a stretch to call the bottle half full at that point.

By then, the sun was beginning to sink in the sky. The wind was growing cold. Even through the whiskey warmth, I felt a chill running through my body. The air off the mountains, cold and damp, came running in front of the impending twilight.

"I can smell the mountains." T took a deep breath.

"Yeah."

"Can you imagine what this sunset would look like from up there? I mean, way up there. Just sitting on the top of the highest damn peak there is and watching the sun go down."

"Sounds great." I poured another gulp of whiskey down my throat. "Really great."

"Let's go see it!"

"Now?" I was pretty drunk at that point.

"Tomorrow."

"Tomorrow?"

"Tomorrow! It'll be great, brother."

"Yeah?" I drank more whiskey.

"Hell yeah, man. We can get up good 'n early, find a path, and head up there. We'll catch the sunset, camp for the night, and then head back down the next day."

"Yeah?"

"Yeah. There's a place not far from here called Grandfather Mountain. You can pay to get on it, but there's also tons of paths you can just climb up for free. The view from the top is supposed to be epic!"

"Epic, you say?" I laughed.

"Yeah, epic, bro."

"Well hey." I took a long sip from the bottle. "Let's do it, then."

"You serious?" T asked. "Don't bull me."

"I'm serious, bro."

"You're in?"

"I'm in."

He smiled and grabbed the bottle from my hand. He tipped it back high. "This, my brother, this is what I meant! An adventure! We're going to climb a damn mountain!"

"We'll look down on the world like we really own it!" I took the whiskey back.

"My friend," he said. "We can piss down on the world like we own it."

We both laughed. We were well past drunk, and filled with youthful exuberance. We were intoxicated with life as much as liquor, back then. The world was ours to conquer, and we would overcome it by sheer force of desire alone.

In those days we never considered failure. We were far removed from the vagaries of such ideas as marriage or careers, much less the misery that their failings entailed. Neither of us would ever get divorced nor go bankrupt. We would never grow old and tired, never find that the thrill of living was gone. The marrow of life was ours from which to suck deep, and we would seize it with clenched fists, reduce it to its lowest terms, and never imagine to let it go. We would cut the broad swath, and to ourselves and to ourselves alone, we would finally give a true account of the sublime experience of life fully lived.

We dreamed of the future, of everything there was to accomplish in the world. Adulthood was far away, yet, and when it was upon us we would surely know. That time might slip away from us was far beyond the scope of our understanding. Time was as endless as all of our dreams could make it, flowing on like an infinite river, and we were borne upon it. We could never grow old. We could never die. It didn't occur to us that there was no line, no defining moment, but that instead adulthood would creep up unnoticed, and by the time we discovered it, it would be too late. We would be worrying about mortgages and 401ks, all the while asking ourselves just where the time had gone.

Back then, none of it was real. The days were long and full of promise. A good friend and a fifth of cheap whiskey was all I needed. It was all I could imagine ever needing, really. Happiness didn't have to be sought out or bought. It simply was.

"T?"

"Yeah, brother?"

"I got an idea."

"What's that?"

"How 'bout we finish this bottle?"

"I figured that was a given."

"That's just the first half of my idea," I said.

"That so?"

"Uh huh."

41

"Got a second half?"

"Uh huh." I tipped the bottle back.

"You gonna tell me, or are you just gonna sit there drinkin' all the whiskey by yourself?"

"Second one sounds good."

He laughed and snatched the bottle from my hand. "If you're not gonna tell me the second half of that idea, then I'm gonna hafta' finish this all by my self."

"F--- you."

"I'll do it."

He tilted the bottle back, pouring the whiskey into his mouth.

"T!"

He continued pouring, gulping the liquor down.

"T!" I yelled. "T, put the bottle down!"

He complied and directed a particularly long burp my way. "Idea?"

"Like I said, first we go ahead and finish what's left of this bottle."

"Yeah, I got that stinkin' part." He was starting to slur his words. I didn't imagine I was sounding any better.

"Okay, okay," I said. "What if, instead of climbing the mountain tomorrow, we just sit on our rumps and don't do a thing? Then, the next day, when we didn't down a whole bottle of liquor the night before, we get up and climb the mountain?"

"My friend," said T. "That is brilliant. Absolutely brilliant."

"I thought so."

He laughed and took another drink. "You and your loopy ideas."

10

By midday the path was no longer subtly steep. The foliage above our head was growing thinner, allowing the sun to shine brighter and brighter upon our backs. The weight of our packs, which had at first barely fazed us, was becoming increasingly burdensome.

"Just why," I asked. "Why did we think it was a good idea to bring canned food?"

"Well," T said. "I figured if we didn't eat for a few days this hike would be pretty miserable."

"Smart a...."

"Look," he said. "Here's how I figure it. We eat the canned stuff first, of course. When we go for the peak, we can just take the water and stash our packs in some bushes or somethin'. We can pick 'em back up on the way down. I mean, hell, it's not like there's anybody out here who's gonna take 'em or anything."

"Yeah," I said. "That'll work."

We continued our hike in silence. I felt a sense of peace wash over me. It felt good, putting the city behind me and striking off into nature. I felt, then, like I could walk the entire Appalachian Trail, carrying everything I needed on my back.

"Hey, T," I called.

"What's up, brother?" He stopped and turned around, about ten yards ahead of me on the path.

"Just been thinkin', man, about everything that went down back in Florida."

"Brother," he said. "Don't do that."

"It's fine." I paused. "Look, T. I just wanted to tell you, man, how sorry I am about everything."

"Don't worry about it."

"I do worry about it, though. Everything... bro, it just got out of hand. I let it get out of hand."

"I knew," he said. "You had a lot goin' on."

"That's no excuse."

"Brother, you didn't do a damn thing to anybody but yourself. You don't need to apologize to me."

"Yes," I insisted. "I really do. I was going down fast, and I dragged you down with me."

"Bullshit."

"It's not."

"It is, and you damrn well know it." He looked me right in the eyes. "Now cut this out, okay?"

"T," I said. "You came down there to help me through everything, and I made a mess of both our lives."

He shook his head and turned back up the trail. I followed a few feet behind him.

"T!"

"I came down there," he said. "Because my best friend got himself a sweet place by the beach that happened to have a spare bedroom. I wanted to be there, brother. We had a great time!"

"You mean I got messed up while you babysat me?"

"You know that's not how it was," he said. "We got messed up. We partied. It was we, brother, not you."

I sighed. "T, man, I'm just sayin'."

"Sayin' what, exactly?"

"Saying I'm sorry that I am whatever the hell it is that I am, whatever you wanna call it."

"You're my friend. That's what I'll call it."

"You know what I mean," I said. "I'm a goddamn destructive whirlwind, tearing through one life at a time."

"Dammit, man, cut the shit! We're both adults. I make my own decisions, good or bad. So, in Florida it went south! So you had some issues to deal with! Man, you're my brother, and I was happy as hell to be there for you. I was happy to be there with you. That's that, seriously."

"All right, T." I clapped him on the back. "I just feel bad about the whole thing, ya' know?"

"I know, brother. It's over, though. It's passed. Let it go."

"Thanks."

He looked over at me and smiled. Up ahead, the trail took a sharp turn to the left. As we rounded the bend we were bathed in sunlight. The trees fell away and the bright blue of the afternoon sky lay naked before us. The mountain mist floated over the distant peaks. A sea of green stretched endlessly below. Nature, in all its boundless glory, lay at our feet.

T was the first to speak. "Holy …."

"Wow." I stood beside him, gazing off the side of the mountain. Behind us the peaks of Grandfather stretched up into the heavens.

"Hell yeah!" T turned to me, excited. "Look at it, brother! The world is ours, from up here. All of it is ours!"

"It's beautiful."

"It's beyond beautiful," he said. "It's absolutely glorious."

He was right. The vision that stretched before us was nothing short of glorious. The trees were bright green and the spring flowers were in full bloom. A river wound down the far mountains and into the valley below. The land was untouched, pristine in its beauty.

"You know what the best part is?" T asked.

"What's that?"

"We're only halfway up!" T was exuberant. "Can you imagine what the view's gonna be like from the top?"

Any misgivings I had about the climb faded away in an instant. Confronted with the transcendent beauty of nature, I felt alive inside. It flowed over me; it flowed through me. "This is where I was meant to be." Those felt like the truest words I had ever spoken.

"When we hit the peak," T said. "My spirit will be truly free."

"Amen, brother."

"You know, for a while there, I didn't think we would ever be able to make this trip."

"I'm sorry," I said.

"That's not what I meant." T laid his hand on my shoulder. "Being up here like this, I feel reborn."

"Yeah?"

"It's a new life for both of us, brother."

"I sure hope so." I laughed. "Cause God knows I made a huge mess of the last one."

T laughed, but it sounded somehow empty. He looked sagely at me. "Make the best of it while you can, my friend. When your time comes, you'll wish you took more time to enjoy the moments like this."

"Way to be depressing," I joked.

"It's not depressing," he responded. "It's just the reality of things."

I looked at him, sadly. At that moment, I was suddenly more deeply aware. I felt the cool wind blowing in my hair and running along the hairs on my arm. I felt the sun shining on my face. I could smell the trees, hear the distant rush of water. My body was weightless, floating high above the soft green grass of the mountainside. For a moment, all the suffering of the world faded to the wayside; for a fraction of a moment, I glimpsed Nirvana. I felt free and open, drunk on life like one of Kerouac's crazy free Bodhisattvas of the deep mind.

The life I had lived, all the mistakes I had made, disappeared for an instant. The future, too, faded away. There was only the present moment, and it was infinite. Love and joy filled my heart; my soul floated above my body. Compassion overcame despair. I felt it deeply. There was compassion for all living things, for all who ever had lived or ever would. There was compassion, even, for myself, in all my broken thoughts. In that unending moment, I knew no fear. The spirit of the world was alive inside me.

The Ranch 11

I remember my second day at The Ranch. It didn't start off feeling any different from the first. I awoke to a light knock on my door, which I promptly ignored. It came a second time, a little louder. And then the door opened, just a crack. It was a different girl from the day before. "Breakfast is in half an hour."

"I'm fine," I said. "Y'all already made me eat dinner last night. That should get me through the day. Not feeling much like eating, right now."

"We're not gonna make you eat, but you do need to get up."

"What for? I'm sick. I'm sleeping today."

"There's coffee in the kitchen, and it's almost time for your meds." The voice was patient, but firm. "They're gonna slow down your taper schedule a little, so it's not so unpleasant for you."

At that, I perked up. "Yeah?"

"Yeah," she answered. "It's only for a few more days, but it'll make things easier on you. We don't want you to be uncomfortable."

"I'm pretty uncomfortable now," I muttered, pushing down my sweat-soaked blankets. I stood up, swayed a little and sat back down on the edge of the bed. My head was spinning, and my legs ached. Even that two seconds of standing was a miserable chore. "Can I get dressed?"

"Half an hour, breakfast." The door closed again. From the other side came, "And if you hurry, we'll get you your meds first, so maybe you'll be able to eat."

I did the best I could to mop up the sweat coating my body and climb into clean clothes. I considered a shower, but the idea of standing up for that long seemed impossible. Instead, I doused myself in deodorant and did the best I could to brush the tangled mess on top of my head and tie it back into a ponytail. Mounting a concerted effort, I grabbed my toiletry kit and stumbled to the bathroom. "Not the kit I usually grab in the morning." I laughed under my breath at my own bad joke.

A few minutes later, I was sitting at a table surrounded by strange faces, trying not to drink or speak as I let the powdery medication tables dissolve against my gums. Then, there were only three others staying at The Ranch, so breakfast was an intimate affair. They laughed and joked with each other, seeming in surprisingly good spirits considered where they were. They were friendly, introducing themselves and telling me the short-form versions of their own stories. My responses were mostly grunts and nods or shakes of the head.

I can't tell you that, on that morning, I remembered any of their names. I couldn't tell you what they looked like or a single bit of what they told me about themselves. In that first day there, I was still awash in a sea of shame and self-pity, and I assumed they visited only those same emotions upon me. By the end of it all, I would know each and every one of their names, and be sure that they would all be lifelong friends. But on that morning, I had no other thought than to avoid dry-heaving at the sight of food while I waited for my medication to take effect.

It wasn't more than fifteen or twenty minutes before I started to feel better, though I would've sworn it had been hours. I managed to take a few smile bites of toast—half a sausage link, even—and wash it all down with orange juice. It was then that I noticed just how desperately thirsty I was, and I proceded to consume another six or seven glasses in a row. The rumble in my stomach told me that was a poor decision, but after the pain I'd been feeling earlier that morning, I wasn't in much of a position to complain any longer.

I managed to get myself into the shower. I washed the filth and sweat from my hair. The thought of shaving my face or trimming my beard seemed overwhelming, so I let that be. I left the bathroom with my hair still soaking wet and my beard an uncombed mess, looking like a mountain main who'd just lost a fight with a river.

The same girl who' woke me up this morning was waiting in the main room of the house. "It's time for group. Down at the barn. Everyone else is already down there."

Now that I was free of the chills and cold sweats that had greeted me when I first opened my eyes in the morning, I felt bad for being so terse earlier. "Thank you." I even tried to fake a smile, though I doubt I did a convincing job of it.

"Down at the bottom of the hill," she said. "Do you need me to walk you down there?"

I shook my head. "I can manage." I stumbled down the hillside to the barn. Feeling a sudden rush of anxiety, I pushed the door open slowly. The three people from breakfast—two men about my age and a woman who looked to be just a few years older—were seated around a long conference table. At the head of the table, pointing towards a white board, was a slender woman with dark hair.

She smiled and motioned towards me. "Come in, sit down! We haven't even gotten started yet."

With my head down, I wandered towards the table and took a seat at the far end. I avoided making eye contact as best I could. I could feel them all looking at me. My heart began to pound in my chest.

"My name is Margot," said the woman. "This is our Mindfulness class." She paused. "I know the few first days are tough, but try not to get caught up in everything. Here, we take it one moment at a time."

"Sure." I still didn't look up.

"Do you want to tell us anything about yourself? About what brings you here, or maybe just a few quick-"

"I'm here because I'm a bungler," I interrupted. "I'm here because I'm a f---- person, who messes up, and I let myself get sent out here so I can't ruin anybody else's life."

"No, you're not."

I felt a hand on my shoulder, but I didn't look up. "You're here to get better. And as long as you keep saying things like that, you're not going to let yourself get better. I don't want to hear it again." There was a sharpness to the last sentence she uttered.

I was in no mood to hear it. I could already feel my eyes swelling with tears again. My response came out barely audible. "You don't know what I am. But I do."

"Well," she said. "We're going to find out who you are. And I promise you, it's not what you think. You've come this far. You've taken a big step already. Now look up, let the light in, and stop trying to destroy yourself. You're suffering, but that doesn't mean you need to force yourself to suffer further."

I looked up. She was smiling at me. Not a wide grin, but a small, empathetic smile. I wiped the tears from my eyes and shook my head.

"Look," she said. "We're here together for a while. If you're so sure you're right, that all you are is a f--- up, then go ahead and prove me right. All that I'm asking is that, since you're here, you give me a chance to prove that it's not true."

"That's a pretty big task to take on."

"You've taken on a big task, too Now, promise me, that if I put everything I have into helping you, you'll put everything you have into helping yourself. Otherwise, you don't need to waste your time here. Nothing is going to change."

"Okay," I said. "I mean, got nothing else to lose, right?" I tried to force out a half- hearted laugh.

"Great," she said, turning and moving back towards the front of the table. "Let's get today started."

12

When we finally picked up our packs to continue our journey, the wind had whipped itself into a frenzy. Far in the distance the blue sky faded into darkening clouds. The air felt thick with moisture, and the hairs on my arm stood on end. I could feel the electricity in the air.

"It smells like rain," I said.

"Looks like it, too," T replied. "Rain and then some. Wha're you thinkin' we should do?"

I shrugged. "Not much to do. I'm not turnin' around because of some rain, if that's what ya' mean."

"I hear you, brother. Gonna be pretty miserable up here if it really starts comin' down, though."

"Well," I said. "Let's go as far as we can. If it gets bad, we'll tent up until it passes."

"Hell yeah, brother." T smiled and clapped me on the back.

"Hey, journey to the total end, right?"

He laughed. "Man, I don't think I've heard you say that one since high school." A pause. "You never should've stopped."

"I know, T." Something about that made me sad as hell. I'd used that phrase all the time when I was younger, almost like a sort of personal motto. It was my own mantra, repeated ad infinitum throughout my teenage years.

"Brother?"

"What's up?"

"You know this isn't the end, right? I mean, even after this trip, there's more out there for ya'."

I don't know what made him say that, but something about it sent a chill down my spine. It hit me, then, that I really hadn't thought about anything beyond reaching the peak. "One thing at a time, T. One day at a time."

He frowned. "I'm just sayin', ya' know. In the end, there's still a world you have to go back to. It kept on moving while you were away, and it's moving now. If you don't hit the ground running, you're gonna fall right back down."

Before I could respond, we were interrupted by the rumbling of distant thunder. Not far away, we could see waves of rain washing over the mountains.

"Let's go!" T shouted. He broke into a jog, moving as best he could with the weight of his pack pressing down on his shoulders.

I followed close behind. The sound of the rain beating down upon the trees moved closer. "T!" I was right behind him, but he couldn't hear me over the swirling winds of our impending doom. "T!"

"Yeah?" He didn't look back.

"This rain's comin' up fast! If we don't tent up really quick, we're gonna be soaked through."

"Not here," he answered. "The path's too narrow and the ground's too soft."

"Damn." I picked up my pace. "We need the map. We gotta find something."

"Back left pocket of my pack." He slowed, slightly, so that I was running right on his heels.

Even as I reached for the pack, the rains caught up to us. It hit like a freight train, coming at us from the open face of the cliffs to our right. A wall of water, pouring down in sheets, smashed into us.

I missed the map on my first attempt. I stumbled for a moment as a torrent of water rushed down the path.

"Careful!" T shouted. He slowed down again, allowing me to catch up.

Half-blinded by the rain beating against my face, I made another grab at the pack. This time, the tips of my fingers just reached the map. I leaned forward, doing the best I could to block the rain with my body.

"Keep up!" T sped up, water splashing against his thighs as his boots pounded against the softening mud.

I studied the map as best as I could in the driving rain. I flipped it back and forth, upside and down, trying to figure out just where the hell we were at. One eye was on the map, while the other was trained on T. I couldn't see more than a few feet in front of me. My hair was matted against my face, directing even more water into my eyes.

"You see anything on there?"

"I still don't even know where we're at. Gimme a goldarn minute to look!"

"Watch your step while you're trying to read that thing," T said.

"Just don't run off the mountain, 'cause I'm following you."

"No promises, brother!" He laughed, even as the wind picked up speed and a river of mud and water threatened to wash us off of the slopes.

The map was starting to come apart in my hands. Finally, I made sense of it enough to figure out where we were. I shifted my full attention downwards, hoping to find some source of shelter before the paper melted away.

"Left!" T shouted as he turned sharply.

My feet drove into the ground, pushing as hard as I could while I fought to maintain my balance. The sheer emptiness of the cliffside appeared before me. There was no valley below, no soft sea of green. My eyes met the endless gray void. There was only swirling mist and torrential spouts of water. The land and sky had become one, and they threatened to swallow me. Mud sprayed behind me as I felt my boots sliding.

I kept my balance, still following T closely. I wasn't so lucky the second time the path turned, this time cutting right and backwards at a forty-five degree angle. I planted my left foot and spun, but my right came down against empty air.

I fell hard, slipping right off of the mountainside. All I could do was swear hopelessly as the ground vanished around me. The map was washed away as I flailed my arms. My hands pulled away long grass and twigs, but found nothing of substance to grasp onto. Time seemed to freeze and the world faded away.

Even as I fell, there was a strange weightlessness to my body. I didn't feel the branches tearing at my skin or the water pouring over me. My wet socks and dripping clothes no longer seemed to touch my body. My pack floated along with me as I was thrown into emptiness. I could hear T's voice above me, shouting. His words were unintelligible.

I hit the side of the mountain and bounced once. The air was forced from my lungs as my stomach slammed into a tree branch. I managed to grab on, slowing my fall just long enough to swing a leg around and plant it against a gnarled root. I hung, precariously, on the side of the mountain. Below me was a sheer drop. It was hundreds of feet, at least, before the mountain rolled outwards and its gradient lessened.

"T!" I clung to the branch with all my strength, trying my best not to look down. The rain still beat against my face. I could barely see.

"Holy …!" He was leaning over the side of the mountain, barely visible through the downpour.

I tried to take stock of my surroundings, but panic still filled my chest. My life hadn't flashed before my eyes; there had been no moment of revelation. There was only shock and confusion, and then weightlessness followed by pain. I struggled to avoid looking down into the depths below.

"Can you hear me?" T's voice just rose above the din of the storm. "Can you talk?"

"Yeah." Speaking was a chore. I was wedged against a sapling that was growing nearly horizontally out of the rocky mountainside, my feet pushing against the roots below. I looked up. I'd fallen at least ten feet down.

"Are you hurt?"

"Dunno."

"I mean, badly hurt?"

"Don't … know!" I shifted my weight, testing the stability of my position. "Ribs hurt."

"Brother, you're lucky you caught on to something."

"Almost didn't." Thunder crashed behind me. The storm was still raging on, showing no signs of relenting.

"Are you… stable?" T asked. "I mean, like, your position."

"I think so," I replied, still shouting. "But I'm afraid if I move I won't be."

He didn't answer. He was still leaning over the edge of the cliff, staring down at me. Lightning raced across the sky above us.

57

For a minute or two, neither of us spoke. I continued shifting my weight, slowly, attempting to determine just how stable my position actually was. My arms were beginning to ache from clinging tightly to the branches.

"Can you get back up?"

"I dunno." I could barely see around me with the rain beating down against my face. I studied the cliff side, searching for some way to climb back up. "I can't see a goldarn thing."

"How can I help?"

"T, I have no idea."

"Well get one!" His voice was suddenly sharp. "This storm's only getting worse, and you can't go down there forever! How the hell can I help?"

"I don't know!"

"Well think!" He snapped. "I can't see you well enough to do a darn thing, so I need your help to tell me what the hell to do. We're getting you back up here."

I managed to turn myself around. Using all my strength, I pulled myself up so that both feet were pressed against the sapling. It bent under my weight. I reached upward, feeling along the mountainside with my hands until I grasped a rock. I pulled up with all my strength, stretching my other hand another foot higher.

"Okay, T," I said. "I'm going to pull myself up as far as I can, but this muddy cliff is going to fall apart. Find somewhere to secure yourself up there so you can reach down to me."

"I've got this," he answered. "If you can reach my hand, I can get you back up." He stretched down over the edge of the cliff. I could see his hand, stretching downward through the rain. He wasn't nearly as far as I'd first thought.

I pulled myself upwards again, searching for another handhold. As I found one, I pushed with all my might against the branches underneath my feet. I heard them crack just as I jumped upwards, attaching myself to the side of the cliff and clinging on for dear life. T's hand was only a foot or two away.

"Bro, you can do this!" He struggled to stretch further. "Come on, closer! If I come down anymore, I'm gonna fall trying to pull you up."

I pushed my feet against the rocks, scrambling up the side of the mountain. My muscles burned as I stretched upward, pulling with every ounce of strength in my body. I felt T's fingers wrap around my wrist.

"Climb, man! Climb and I'll pull!"

I did as he said. I felt the muddy cliff side beginning to fall apart as the rocks tore into my legs. I stretched with my other arm, gripping the lip of the trail as T pulled upward with all his might. Moments later, he had a second hand beneath my armpit, and then I was back on solid ground, gasping for air. Every muscle in my body cried out in pain. Blood streamed down my legs.

"No resting yet, brother." He pulled me to my feet. "Get up, get up. Let's get to the spot and get inside the tent, and then we can patch you up."

I grinned at him as the realization hit me that I was, in fact, alive and standing on solid ground. Once again, my pack was still attached to my shoulders. "I'm alive. I'm really alive!"

"Yeah," he said. "man. Yeah, you are." He reached an arm around and grabbed under my shoulder to help me walk. We stumbled forward, half-blinded by the rain. We forced our way up the path, heading towards the sheer side of a cliff face that looked to offer some measure of protection against the fury of Nature.

13

We managed to set up our tent on the closest thing we could find to flat ground. The mountain at our backs blocked the worst of the rain as we sat huddled inside, the storm still raging around us. For the second time in as many days, I found myself changing into dry clothes. This time, there would be no fire to warm me.

It was a while before either of us spoke. I sat there shivering, wrapped in every dry layer I had left, while T stared numbly at the tent floor. His eyes never shifted. They were focused entirely downward, a pained expression stretched across his face.

"You okay, T?"

"This is bad, man." He shook his head. "We're soaked through and this whole damn mountain's a pile of mud."

I wanted to agree with him. I was cold and wet and miserable, but something about the defeat in his voice spurred me in the opposite direction. "Well … ignore the cold and dismiss the mud, then. Peak's still there."

He shot me a sidelong glance. "You try to get anywhere close to that peak, and you will end up falling off the damn mountain."

"Says who?"

"Says logic!" His eyes were still locked onto the floor. "There's no way you're getting anywhere near that peak. It's all a damn mess. You think this impossible mountain is worth dyin' for?"

I shrugged. "Lives have been lost for lesser things."

"Don't give me that bullshit," he said. "You're not going to die over getting to the top of that mountain."

"T." I put a hand on his shoulder. "You and I both know, I damn near died ten times over for far stupider reasons. At least this has meaning!"

"Meaning?" He scoffed. "What meaning?"

"Whatever meaning we want," I said. "We'll make our own meaning. Hell, I dunno about you, but to me there's as much meaning in getting to the top of this darn mountain as there has been for anything else I've done."

He looked up at me, but said nothing.

"Look, man," I said. "This whole thing, this climb... It means whatever the hell we want it to mean, right? It's just you and me, and if we do it or don't do it, nobody else is ever gonna know for sure. But me and you, we'll know. We'll know we made it. We'll know we beat the odds. We'll know that we stood up and screamed at the top of our lungs, 'This mountain is ours to conquer!' We'll know, and we'll remember, and that's all the goddamn meaning I need. So yeah, yeah, this does mean something."

I could see a smile creeping up upon the corners of his lips. "So what does it mean, then?"

"It means," I said, without hesitation, "whatever we want it to. It means nothing. It means everything. It means you and me set out to conquer Grandfather, and he threw every bit of rain and plague at us that was within his power, and we persevered. It means we beat the damn mountain!"

"Is that really what it means, brother?"

"What're you getting at, T?"

He shrugged. "I don't know. If I knew, I wouldn't have asked the question."

I didn't answer.

He looked up at me. "So what does it mean?"

"It means," I said. "That I'm not a failure. It means that, for once in my life, I set out to do something and I actually did it."

"You've never been a failure, brother."

"Are we talking for real here, or are we just bullshitting around, T?"

"You tell me."

"We both know what I am, T. We both know what I've done. We know the chances I blew, the things I've messed up, the lives I've torn apart because they got caught up in my goldarn downward whirlwind."

He looked at me, but said nothing.

"Look, man," I sighed. "We can sit and debate on this and we're not gonna' get anywhere."

"Why the hell not?"

"You're frustrating, T."

"You," he said, his voice rising suddenly, "need to stop with all your goddamn bullshit. You keep talking about what you are and what you've done like every person in this world hasn't made a damn mistake or two or ten. You wanna know what I think you are?"

"Don't bullshit me, T."

"I never do, my friend."

"I feel like you're about to."

"Well," he said. "You feel wrong, then. I don't know what else to tell you, really."

"Tell me, then, T," I responded. "What am I? Because from where I'm standing, I'm a damn near thirty year old man-child who's never accomplished a thing. I'm an aging screw-up who's skated by on some damned fool notion that I'm smarter than everyone around me and somehow different. The damn rules don't apply to me, right? I can throw away a college scholarship and drop out. I can fill my body full of whatever bullshit I can get into my veins. I can drink and drink and quote books I read ten years ago. I can be Neal Cassady, the life of the party, like a trained bear, and then when the shtick has gotten old and everyone around me has fulfilling careers and wives and kids and whatever the hell it is they've been working towards, I can be dancing around drunk spouting stupid jokes and rambling on about some goddamn pseudo-intellectual philosophies cobbled together from whatever quotes I cherry-picked to support my own juvenile views on life. That, T, that is what I am."

He looked me right in the eyes, staring silently for several moments. He spoke slowly, choosing his words with care. "That... that's really what you think? 'Cause man, I'm tellin' you, from where I'm at, that's not what I see."

This time, I was the one who remained silent. I really wasn't sure what else to say, and all of it was starting to weigh heavily on my shoulders. The last thing I wanted to be was a walking pity-party, climbing halfway up a mountain just to whine about my mistakes and failures. I couldn't shake the feeling, though, that I really meant every word I said.

"My friend," said T, "we've had talks like this before. Hell, I think everyone's felt like you do, at one point or another. God knows I have. But the truth of it all is, right now we're here on this mountainside, and the whole world is in front of you. From this point, you can go wherever you want and do whatever you want to do. Make this point, right here, right now. Make this the starting point. Whatever it is you think you've done, whatever it is that you wish you could change or want to forget... just let it go."

"It's not that easy," I answered. "You don't just let everything go. I don't get to just open my eyes one day and say, 'Hey, world! I'm not a mess-up anymore!' It doesn't work like that."

"Why the hell not?"

"Because it just doesn't."

"Why?"

"What the hell do you mean, why?"

"My brother," T said. "Stop for a minute, okay?"

"Yeah, okay."

"Why can't it be like that? You think you're a f---up, I get that. So change! Wake up and make that decision that today is gonna be different." T put his hand on my shoulder. "And don't go telling me I'm full of it, because I can read your mind."

I stayed silent.

"Yesterday's done, man. Whatever the hell it is you think you've done... I mean, you can't go back and change it, right? It's done, it's written. If you sit and worry and piss yourself about all these mistakes you think you made, it doesn't get you–or anyone else–anywhere. So, take what you can get from it... and then decide. Decide that today is different. What else can you do, right?"

"It's not that easy, T."

"Goddammit, it is!" He said. "You make it that easy! You decide. That's it, you decide. Nobody else decides how you feel except for you. So get your ass up and either decide to be better–in whatever way you think you need to be better–or just sit there and wallow in the past and be freaking miserable and useless to everyone."

I felt pretty stupid just then, like a child being scolded. Mostly, though, I felt stupid because I knew he was right.

65

"Look, man," he continued. "I'm not trying to be hard on you. I'm not trying to be a dick. But this is how things are, right? Whatever the hell has happened, man, it's done. Nothing is gonna change any of that. But you can decide what happens from here."

"Well," I said. "I guess we better decide to get some sleep, then, because we've got a big mountain to climb in the morning."

14

T had arrived in Florida before our first attempt on the mountain just after lunchtime on a Thursday. I was there to pick him up at the airport terminal, decked out in a bright blue Hawaiian shirt and sandals, sporting a beard I hadn't trimmed for at least a month and a half. I pulled my car up to the curb, beer in hand. "Brother, brother! How ya' doin'?"

He had a single duffel bag slung across his shoulder and a big wide smile stretched all the way across his face. "I'll be great if you tell me that ya' got a beer for me."

I motioned to a cooler sitting behind the driver seat. "Like I'd pick you up with anything less than an ice cold twelve pack."

"That's my boy!" He hopped into the car and tossed his bag in the backseat. "Let's go!"

"Where's the rest of your stuff?"

"That's it, man. One bag's enough."

"You serious?" I asked. "You shipping the rest of your stuff or what?"

"Nah." He grinned. "That's it, brother."

"You're tellin' me," I said. "That everything you own is in that one little bag?"

He shrugged. "I got what I need in there."

"What the hell happened to the rest of your stuff?"

"I left it in the old apartment. Forget it Anyway, stuff's just stuff, right?"

I laughed. "Talk about moving across the country with nothin' but the clothes on your back."

"Stuff's just stuff." He repeated. "I just left the rest of it in the apartment. Not worth the trouble of trying to hold on to it. If I decide I want new stuff, I'll get new stuff."

"If?"

"Hell, I dunno, man. I don't need any of that."

"If you say so." I pulled my car off the curb and wove my way through the airport traffic and headed east. I cranked up the radio, rolled down the windows, and lit a cigarette. When the ocean came up in front of me, I turned the car north and gunned the engine up A1A. "Hey, buddy, at least you get the scenic view on this drive."

"Better than the highway, my brother." T grinned and slapped me on the back. He took a long drink from his beer and peered out the window. "So where we goin'?"

"Well," I said. "I figured we'd get back to the place and let you put your stuff away, kind of get the lay of things."

"No!" He exclaimed. "I'll have plenty of time to see the place. I'll be living there."

"Hell, buddy, I know you've been traveling since way too early in the damn mornin'. We can get back there, get you settled in, and let ya' get some rest."

"F ... that." He opened another beer. "Let's go do something fun! Hell, man, it was cold up there. It's a beautiful day here! Take me to the beach. I'll buy you a beer."

I shook my head a little bit. "I should probably take you back to the place, let you get settled in. We can do somethin' a bit later on, maybe."

My eyes were locked on the road, but I could feel his stare. "What the hell's wrong with you?" He asked.

"Nothin', man. Nothin." I glanced over at the clock and sped up.

68

"Since when do you say no to stopping for a beer? Besides, man, it's been too damn long! We got some catchin' up to do."

"Yeah," I said. "Yeah, T. I'm fine with that. Just not right now. In an hour or two, we'll go. I know some places you'll like. I'll show you some great places." I glanced over at the clock again. "I'll drop you off at the place, and you get settled. We'll go in an hour or two. We'll have a great time."

"Drop me off?"

"Yeah. That cool?"

"Brother," he said. "What the hell is going on with you?"

"Nothin, T." My hands were shaking as I struggled to light a cigarette. I wiped the sweat from my forehead.

He sipped on his beer in silence for a minute or two, gazing out the window at the endless blue of the south Florida sky. "I don't need to get settled. You don't need to drop me off. I can see the place later."

"We're almost there. Just for an hour or so. I'll be back."

"Where the hell you planning to go?"

The light in front of us turned red. I glared at it and said nothing. I tapped my left foot impatiently against the floorboard. "C'mon c'mon, change," I said to the stoplight. As soon as it turned, I slammed on the gas. I glanced down at my phone. "We're almost there. Don't worry."

"I'm not worried about gettin' there," he said. I didn't have to look over to know the smile had faded from his face. "I am wonderin' what the hell is goin' on, though."

"Look, man, don't worry about it. I just gotta run and take care of somethin' real quick."

"I'll come with you. I don't mind."

I shook my head. "You don't need to come with me. Just trust me, okay? I'll be back quick. I'll probably be less than an hour."

"Will you just tell me what the f…'s goin' on?"

I scratched at the crook of my elbow. Sweat was dripping down my face. I fiddled with the air conditioner.

"You're sweating up a storm, brother."

"Yeah. Hot in here." I shivered.

I knew he was frowning. "You've got the A/C goin' full blast."

"Yeah." Another red light. I slapped the steering wheel in frustration, staring down at my phone, then back up the clock.

"You okay?" T asked. "You're watching the damn clock more than the road."

"It's fine. I'm fine." The light turned green and I slammed on the gas. "Just got somethin' I need to take care of."

"Jesus, dude," he said. "Stop with the bullshit. Whatever the hell you gotta' do, just go do it. You don't have to drop me off. I don't mind comin' along. Really."

"Then, fine." The brakes squealed in protest as I pushed on them hard, pulling the car into a u-turn. I ignored the blaring of horns from all around me. "Pass me a beer?"

"Uh huh." I knew his eyes were fixed on me as he passed me the can. "You're really sweating."

"Yeah. Don't feel so good." I drained the beer with my right hand while I kept my left on the wheel. I lit a cigarette and rolled down the window.

After a few minutes, T spoke again. "So, where we goin'?"

I shook my head. "Mind grabbin' me one more beer?"

"Yeah, no problem," he answered. "As soon as you tell me where we're going."

"Just a few miles south, down to Hollywood."

"What's in Hollywood?"

I shook my head in response, taking another drag off my cigarette. I could feel sweat soaking through my undershirt. "Just gotta go see a buddy of mine real quick. Then we can hit the beach, yeah?" I forced a smile.

I didn't have to look to know he wasn't smiling back. "Okay, bro."

We sped on down the road, the car filled with an awkward silence. It was probably the first awkward silence T and I had ever experienced in the nearly thirty years we'd known each other. I left the air conditioner cranked full blast. I continued to sweat.

The sun was still shining bright, but the scenery around us bad began to change. The expansive beachfront mansions of A1A had been replaced by small one-story houses in various levels of disrepair. The straw-roofed patio bars and exclusive marinas were exchanged for dive bars and crumbling restaurants. I pulled off onto a side street, watching with care to make sure no one followed behind me.

"Well, this is a change." T had just opened another beer. He was reclined in his seat, staring out the window with interest as we traveled from opulence into desperation. There was no hint of trepidation in his voice. Instead, he was staring in fascination as he watched society crumble over the course of several miles.

I pulled the car against the curb in front of a particularly empty looking house. There were no cars in the driveway. The blinds were drawn tight. No light peaked out from inside. "Give me five, ten minutes max. Okay?"

"F… it, I wanna come in."

"T."

"Yeah, man?"

I stared directly at him. "Trust me. Not this time, okay? It might get us both into shit."

He nodded. I knew he understood what I meant. The view from the car outside would have to be enough to satiate his curiosity.

"I dunno about you, I just don't feel like seeing either of us get shot today."

"Yeah," he said. "I gotcha, brother. Do what you gotta do. Just, hey, one thing?"

"What's that?" I asked.

"Please, don't leave me sitting out here for long. This neighborhood is sketchy."

"I won't," I promised. "In and out. I'll be quick."

"Do what you gotta do," he repeated. "I trust you, brother."

Before he was done talking, I was out of the car, heading for the door of the house. It was open before I knocked. Wordlessly, I slipped inside. I reappeared not more than two or three minutes later. I immediately lit a cigarette and scurried back into my car. Before T could even buckle his seat belt, we were back on the road. I was no longer sweating.

"You good?" T asked.

"Great, yeah, great," I said. I pulled another cigarette from my pack and lit it off the end of the first. "Wanna hand me a beer?"

He started to say something, but instead simply handed me a beer in silence.

"It's a beautiful day," I said, alternating between my cigarette and my beer. "You still wanna go get a drink by the beach or what?"

"We can do that," he said. "But first, now that you seem to be feeling better, ya' wanna tell me what the hell we were just doing there?"

"T, don't worry about it. It's not a big deal."

"I didn't say it was," he said. "But hell, what if I wanted some of what you got? Hey, brother, I can figure this out. I'm not stupid, and you know I'm not here to judge."

The smile disappeared from my face. "You don't. You don't want any. Trust me."

"You don't know that," he answered. "Hey, man, I'm down to party! You just gotta tell me what's goin' on."

"I'm not partying, T. This... it's not... Listen, just trust me, okay?"

"Man, I'm just sayin'-"

"T, if you wanna party, I can get us something to party with. I'm down for a party. This isn't a party, though. Don't mess with this, okay?" My eyes were only half open. I lit another cigarette.

"You're not making any sense."

"I'm making perfect sense, T. I am. I know I am. Come on, bro, crack open another beer and let's hit the beach! I know this sweet spot, up in Deerfield. This patio bar. It's right on the water. Drinks are solid. Food is awesome. View can't be beat. Right there on the water. Get to feel the wind in your hair and smell the salt and pound some drinks! Man, let me tell you, it's a helluva spot. Helluva spot, right there on the water. It's a drive, but it's worth it. We can head on up there, sit right outside by the beach, order fresh seafood, and get ourselves some of those drinks with f…in' umbrellas in 'em! Sounds great, right?"

"Okay," T said.

In that moment, I could sense he let it go. I wasn't quite sure why; I knew it wasn't gone for good. But the truth of the matter was, in that moment, I couldn't be bothered to care about the why. "So drinks, then?"

"So you're feeling better, then?"

"I'm feeling great," I said. "And look brother, I'm sorry... I don't wanna sketch you out. It's just, ya' know, I got some things I gotta work through. I'm not perfect, ya' know. But I'm working on it, I am. I really am."

"Yeah, man," he said. "I know. Like I said, you know I don't judge. Just let me know if you need anything, okay? I mean, really. Don't pull that junk you like to pull and refuse to say a damn thing to anybody about anything. I'm here, okay? I'm not gonna keep sayin' it, but you gotta know it."

"T," I said. "You got this all wrong, you do. I'm good. I really am. It's just, it's just been a rough day. A rough week, really. Just all kinds of stuff goin' on, lots of trouble on my mind. This isn't me—I mean, me, I'm not normally like this, you know."

"I know," he said. "Look, don't get all worried about me or what I say. I know you know how to handle your own garbage."

"Yeah," I agreed. "Yeah, I do." We fell silent, then. We each cracked another beer, staring out the open windows as the ocean sped by on our right.

"I didn't realize how much I missed the ocean until I saw it again," T said. "It's really great down here."

"It is, right!" I said, cigarette hanging from my lips. "It's a beautiful day, it is. It just doesn't get much better than this. It's a perfect day to go sit by the water and have some drinks, right?" I felt great.

"Yeah," T said. "Let's go get some drinks, brother. I wanna see this place you were going on about. It better be good."

"It is, it is," I said. "Trust me."

"I always do."

15

I awoke now early in the morning to a new world. It was cool and damp as the first light of the sun crawled across the horizon. A light wind brushed along my cheeks as I stepped out into the light of sunrise on the mountainside. T and his pack were nowhere to be seen, but I didn't think much of it, and went about some semblance of a morning routine as best as I could manage. My heart felt strangely light as I soaked in the soft joy of waking up high above the sleeping world.

I made myself as clean and comfortable as I could, and then set to making a small breakfast. I lit a cigarette and gazed out over the misty valleys. I felt awake and alive. The anxiety that I wore like a second skin was, for the moment, nowhere to be found. My mind wandered as I sat on a log and smoked.

I didn't think so much about the last couple of years. I didn't think so much about everything that I usually thought about. Maybe I just didn't think much at all. Images sort of floated through my head, but they were untainted by memory and regret. They simply were.

I remembered camping along the river as a boy and Christmases spent at my grandparents' house. I remembered warm days by the ocean and cool evenings spent on the porch. It all just floated past me in a seemingly endless and unrelated stream. I didn't stop to consider the memories or thoughts. They simply were, as I simply was, there on the side of a mountain enjoying a cool, beautiful morning.

I sat and smoked and let the memories wash over me. It was a funny thing, for me, to feel like that. I'd always thought that maybe there was something wrong with me, because I found myself incapable of enjoying my memories. Sure, I loved to sit at the bar and recount tales of youth and stupidity from the years past. But real memories, even the happy ones—the way my grandfather's voice sounded or playing in the yard with my friends as a kid— always had a way of making me sad. It was like there had always been this thought with me that life was somehow circular, that nothing was really done and no one was really gone. One day, I would do it all again. I would experience every joy over again, and this time I would savor it.

It was only as I got older that it really sank in that sometimes things are just gone for good. Certain times are gone; certain people are gone. And then, it all started to make me sad. I missed everyone and everything. The smell of spring on the breeze was no longer a promise of good things to come, but a vicious reminder of all the other Springs that would never come again. The sad memories made me sad, and the happy ones made me miserable.

Today, though, was different. It was a strange and beautiful thing for me, to feel like this. I smoked my cigarette and remembered running around my grandparents' house and smiled. I took a sip of my water and thought of my parents and those early childhood days when everything seemed so idyllic and perfect, and I felt joy in my heart. I thought of all my friends, of all the good times, and for once I wasn't sad that we weren't as close and the times had moved on. I turned my memories over in my mouth. They tasted light and sweet, and I savored the flavor. My heart didn't flutter when I thought of where I had been. Somehow, in that moment, the idea that life was circular had come back to me. It had crept wordlessly back into my soul, and I knew it as truth, that all the joy I had experienced was still with me, and that I would feel it again. I saw my old friends and lovers, felt the warmth of their smiles and laughed at forgotten jokes. All those I had loved, I would love again, and they would love me still in turn.

It was a beautiful way to feel on such a perfect morning. I became suddenly intensely aware of everything around me. Every smell, every noise was brighter and more pure. I loved the wind and the dew and the warmth of the rising sun. I loved the smell of the blossoming flowers and the feel of the grass on my bare feet. For a single endless moment, I didn't feel shame or regret. I didn't worry. In that moment, I simply existed, and the act of drawing breath was itself the encapsulated sum of all beauty in the world.

When I finally moved, I felt free and unencumbered. My limbs were light and my breaths were easy. I didn't feel sore or exhausted. I wandered back toward the tent. Then I stood outside for a minute, gazing straight up at the sky. The serenity of the morning was still with me, and I felt like a holy offering to some ancient, beautiful spirit of the air itself.

I pulled aside the flap of my tent and, kneeling, dragged my pack into the doorway. I perused its contents, contemplating each item. As I reached the bottom, I found my precious bottle of scotch, still intact despite everything that had happened. Beneath it was a small wooden box. I drew it from the pack, turning it over in my hands. It was made of dark, smooth wood, unmarred by any decoration. I stared at it for a moment and ran my fingers along it, tracing along the edges. I stared at it in silence, and then put it back into my pack. Carefully, I tucked the scotch back inside next to it, and put my clothes and supplies back inside.

I walked back towards the cliff side, the image of the small, plain box still in my head. My happiness had not faded; my soul still felt light. Despite it all, though, I felt a tear forming at the corner of my eye as I stood there, reveling in the pristine beauty of the morning. I didn't have to close my eyes to see the box. It hovered in my vision, itself a part of every tree and flower that I gazed upon.

I pushed it from my mind and breathed in deeply. I looked over my shoulder, staring upward at the peak. In the morning light, it looked closer than ever; it seemed more attainable than ever. When we had began our first journey, it had glared down at us. It had dared us to challenge it. Now, I felt as if it beckoned to us. Its fingers extended along the path, reaching out to us. I smiled up at the face of Grandfather high above and set to packing up camp.

The Ranch 16

At first, I had felt uncomfortable out at the Ranch. About a week into my stay there, things began to feel just slightly different. I was still sullen and withdrawn, spending most of my free time holed up in my room reading, making sure I made use of the scenic trails wrapped around the property only when I was sure no one else would be on them. I ate my meals quietly and quickly, and spent most of the group sessions speaking as little as possible, keeping my thoughts and feelings to myself. But as the medications were halted one by one, and I began to feel the color returning to my cheeks, I found myself occasionally and unexpectedly opening my mouth.

I was sitting down in the barn, our group joined by a few new faces since the week before. I'd cried, whether a lot or a little, at almost every one of Margot's classes up until that point. On this particularly cool October morning, there was a kid who had only shown up a day or two earlier sitting on the other side of the table, arguing furiously with Margot. Since his arrival, he'd alternated between torrential outbursts of tears and furious fits of anger. At the moment, he was strongly favoring the latter.

We were all fairly unfazed by meltdowns at this point. Everyone had one, here or there, as the reality of things set in. Mostly, it was of the crying variety, but anger certainly wasn't uncommon. "This is all f...ing bullshit!" he was shouting. "You can't tell me there's no past and no future and I'm just here right now. No, man, that's stupid. That's... that's a lie, a f...ing lie! There was a yesterday, and there will be a tomorrow, and I'll still be here in this f...ing room listening to all your bullshit!" His face was bright red, and we were all fairly certain at that point that he was getting ready to run out of steam.

"Listen," Margot said, her voice calm as she did her best to force him to make eye contact. "You need to calm down and think about what I mean. When you're letting your anger get the best of you, nothing is going to make ..."

"Make sense," he shouted. "Because it's bullshit. You're bullshit. This place is bullshit!" He stood up, kicking his chair out from beneath his legs. The entire room tensed up. Two of us stood up, slowly and carefully, wondering if he was about to launch himself across the table.

He took short, sharp breaths. Sweat was pouring down his face. His eyes were wide and wild as he stared at Margot across the table. "Bullshit," he muttered under his breath, struggling for gasps of air.

She stared back at him, not breaking eye contact. "You can leave, now."

"You're not telling me what to do. Everyone here is telling me what to do all the time. I think that..."

"Leave!" She barely had to raise her voice, but her gaze remained steady.

It was as if a bucket of water had been thrown into the fire in his eyes, dousing the furious flames and leaving only a smoking, defeated husk. He lowered his head. "Okay." We could all hear him sniffling as he walked towards the door. Just as he reached the door handle, he stopped. He didn't turn around, speaking barely above a whisper. "M, can I still come back tomorrow?"

"Yes," she replied. "Go get some rest. You're excused for the day."

We were all silent for a few minutes. None of us were in a place to judge. One day, about three or four days in, I'd flung my books across a class for no real reason and stormed off to spend the next six hours hiding in the silent darkness of my room. These were not easy times.

M broke the silence. "You might not believe it," she said. "But that might've been the best thing that could happen to him. Did you see the look in his eyes? He thought he hated me. For a second, maybe he did. Not disliked me, but truly and completely hated me. And really, it wasn't because of anything I said. It was because of what was inside him. He saw something he didn't like. And then he let it go." She paused, looking at each of us in turn. "That's part of why you're here, to get it all out. On the outside, you don't keep a job if you have a breakdown like that. You get kicked out of school. But here, when we're healing, it has to come out."

We all nodded, but nobody said anything. We all savored the silence. It wasn't thick and tense like before. It was comforting, a vessel to allow our own thoughts to deliver themselves deep into our hearts. "Remember," she said. "The past is done. The past is only depression. The future... it's not here yet. The future is only anxiety. But this moment, this very moment right here. We're in this moment, and we can make it anything we want. So, what do you want this moment … right now … to be?"

17

Several hours had passed and there was still no sign of T. I finished packing up camp and resumed my customary activity of sitting on a log and smoking, allowing my mind to drift in the breeze. As time passed, my mind shifted from the past back to the present. "Where the hell is T?" I asked out loud.

The mountain gave no answer.

I rose to my feet and wandered back towards the path. "T!" I called. My voice echoed against the peaks, but no answer came, save for the chirping of birds. I walked further, scanning up and down the path for any signs of movement, but saw nothing.

Suddenly, I felt terribly alone up on the mountain. I felt the familiar pull of anxiety tugging at my shirt sleeves. I felt it deep inside my stomach. The whole wide world stretched out around me, endless and green as the morning mists lifted. The only footprints I could locate along the muddy trail were those made by my own meandering steps.

"T!" I called louder this time, but the answer was the same. I shook my head and attempted to push the worry from my mind. He was simply wandering, I told myself, as he was wont to do. I walked further down the path, expecting at each bend to find him standing alongside the trail gazing out over the edge of the world. At each turn, I was disappointed.

The feelings of peace and serenity that had filled my morning were quickly fading away. My heart began to beat faster as I called louder and louder into the empty air. "T!" I shouted. "T, where the hell are you?"

Once again, the mountain gave no answer.

I walked up the path a quarter mile or so, and then back down the same distance from my starting point. I saw nothing. I heard nothing. Deep inside my stomach, I could feel a gnawing sensation arising as anxiety gripped me firmly by the shoulders.

"T! Brother, if you're f...in' with me, this isn't funny." The sensation in my stomach began to congeal as anxiety turned to panic. The distant peaks no longer smiled down at me, but instead gazed with mocking faces.

I retraced my steps back to camp, but found the site untouched. My pack still leaned against the tree where I'd left it. The soft ground remained untouched, marred only by my own footprints.

For a moment I stood still, measuring my breathing even as my heart raced. I scanned the treeline. I saw nothing. Not a sign of anyone. "T!" I didn't expect an answer, this time.

I walked back down the path one way and then the other. I gazed out over the mountainside for any hint of disturbed brush. Again, I saw nothing.

I took a long, deliberate breath and lit a cigarette. *Inhale deep. Exhale slow.* I passed back through the site of our camp, this time taking care to note every detail. I circled the edge of the small clearing and attempted to stay calm. I sat back on a log. I smoked again. Time froze for me as scenarios turned over in my mind. None were pleasant.

In that moment, I felt like the only person in the world. I'd felt like that before, in those early mornings when I woke up before dawn. Then, it was a somber but pleasant feeling. I rose with the sun to drive the streets alone, and the world belonged to me and only me. The roads and the sky were mine the same. The sun climbed over the horizon only to gaze down upon me, master of my own beautifully desolate paradise. My past transgressions faded into the darkness and the east. I alone existed to write the narrative of the waking world, and I would weave a story of endless poetic peace.

Today, that was not my feeling. Today, the world expanded around me, and with each passing mile there was only greater emptiness. The landscape was not mine to enjoy. It was a crushing enemy, making me ever smaller as it stretched in every direction. I grew more insignificant and powerless as every second ticked by. Once again, the faces of the mountain mocked me. Grandfather spit down upon my presence, ready to crush a tiny flea beneath his ancient stone heel. The world was open, but not with possibilities. There was only unending loneliness. I would disappear on this mountain, alone and unknown.

My thoughts and feelings would be reduced to nothing. Every adventure I'd undertaken, every heartwarming moment of human empathy, everything I'd ever said and done and not written down, it would all disappear from existence. The unwritten pages and half thought poems that never touched paper would have just as well never existed. Every secret that I'd kept would be gone, because there would be no one left to remember. This whole climb, every moment of triumph, would mean nothing, because T and I would be gone and there would be no one to know it had ever even happened. It would all pass away and the world would go on as if it had never existed at all. The thoughts consumed me. The world continued to grow. I continued to shrink. Alone on the side of the mountain, I could hardly listen to my own thoughts. All I could hear, echoed in my head, was the same mantra of despair: *none of this matters.*

"I can't f...ing do this to myself." I forced myself to my feet. I lit a cigarette. For a moment, I thought of the scotch tucked away at the bottom of my pack. That thought, too, I pushed from my mind. "T!" Now was not the time to wallow in a cesspool of my own feelings of inadequacy.

I struck back down the trail, and then up once again. I forced a renewed vigor into my steps. *Fake it 'till you make it, dammit.* I continued to call out to T as I walked. I marched with purpose. As the sun climbed higher above the horizon, I found myself once again circling back to camp.

I sat for a moment to catch my breath, leaning my back up against a tree. I closed my eyes. The anxiety and panic had sapped away my energy.

"You okay?" The voice boomed across the clearing.

I opened my eyes, unsure if I'd fallen into some sort of delirious daydream. From back behind the tent, T was striding towards me, the same giant grin as always stretched across his face.

"You all right over there, brother?" He asked. "You got a terrible look on your face."

I wanted to be furious, but instead I was overcome by relief. "Where the hell have you been, T?"

He shrugged. "I've been around. Just checkin' out the woods, lookin' at the paths. You know. Didn't wanna wake ya' up. Figured after yesterday, you could use to sleep in a bit."

"Hell, T. I've been looking for you for hours."

"Have you?" He glanced upwards at the sun. "It didn't feel like that long. Time doesn't mean so much these days, ya' know?"

"Buddy, you scared the heck out of me. There wasn't a sign of you. I swear, I thought you were gone."

"Nah, brother," he said. "Not gone. You know I'm never far away."

I lit a cigarette and tried to shake off the way I felt. The panicked emptiness of the morning still lingered. "You scared the sh.. out of me," I repeated.

"Sorry, brother." His gaze shifted around the campsite. "Looks like you got everything pretty much packed up, huh?"

"Yeah."

"I would've helped."

"Don't worry about it," I said. "It wasn't so bad. Sun came up nice and bright and dried out all that mud, so it just sort of shook right off of everything. Most of our stuff's in pretty good shape."

He nodded. "Yeah, we got lucky. That storm could've really botched up everything up a lot worse than it did. There's some trees down in the woods not that far away. Dunno if it was wind or lightning or what, but it's a mess out there. Our tent could easily be torn to pieces right now."

"Yeah, man," I said. "I'm glad all that happened was-"

"Shhh!" T interjected. He lowered his voice. "Did you hear that?"

"Hear what?" I said, my voice rising just above a whisper.

"Not sure," he said. His eyes flitted nervously back and forth. "I swear, though, I heard something."

"What kind of something?"

"Not sure."

"That's helpful."

87

"Bro, I'm not f…..tin' around." He gave a nervous glance over his shoulder. I raised a cigarette to light it. T slapped it out of my hand. "Don't do that right now."

"T," I said. "the hell is going on?"

This time, I heard it, too. There was a crash in the woods, just beyond the edge of the treeline. Branches snapped, and the high branches of the trees shook. Our eyes were transfixed on the far edge of the clearing. We waited.

The air, thick with moisture, was still. I could feel sweat beginning to bead up on my forehead.

T spoke first. "I don't think that's a person. That didn't sound like a person."

"I don't think so, either," I said. My heart dropped as the realization hit me that my pack was still in the middle of the campsite, halfway to the edge of the treeline.

"We should go," T said."

"My pack." The words felt dry and thick in my mouth. Whatever was crashing unseen in the woods, I had no desire to see it up close.

"Maybe it's just a deer," T offered. He didn't believe himself any more than I did.

"I've never seen deer up here," I said. "Do they even have deer up here?"

"Dunno."

"It's big, T. It's something big."

"Yeah." His voice was shaking.

"I don't wanna find out what it is," I said. "But we gotta get that pack." I took half a step forward. My legs were trembling.

The trees at the edge of the clearing shook violently. The sound of large steps crashing reverberated throughout the trees. I took another step forward. It took everything I had just to will myself forward. Fifteen yards remained between me and the pack.

"I'm thinking I should just run for it," I said.

T shook his head violently, his eyes never straying from the edge of the clearing. "Don't... run."

I took a hesitant step forward, then another. My vision remained locked forward as, inch by inch, I made my way to the pack. My hands shook as I grabbed the leather straps, pulling it slowly over my shoulders.

The closest trees shook. A large shape, barely hidden in shadow, moved just behind them. An unmistakable roar bellowed forth. The trees shuddered.

I backpedaled. Behind me, I could hear T's voice.

"Slow, brother. Nice and slow."

"Slow sounds pretty bad right now."

"I know," T said. "But come on, nice and slow. Turn around and walk. I'll keep an eye on... it."

I turned my back to the woods. In front of me was T, and just behind him, the path. I walked in slow, measured steps. I swallowed hard, feeling a growing lump in my throat. Anxiety had turned to terror deep in the pit of my stomach.

T's eyes widened. "Don't move."

I stopped, unable to see behind me. I focused on T's suddenly pale face. "What do you see?"

He didn't answer. I could see the terror on his face.

"T!" I hissed.

"Just don't move," he whispered. "I don't know if it sees us."

"What is it?" I asked again.

"It does, it sees us. Don't move."

"T, what sees us? You're scaring the hell out of me."

"I think that's appropriate right now."

89

Branches snapped loudly behind me. Massive footsteps pounded against the ground. I fought the urge to look over my shoulder. "T. , T. What's behind me?"

Silently, he mouthed a single word. "Bear."

18

It was a particularly dreary, muggy morning in mid August, more than a few months into our stay in Florida. It rained all night, coming down in torrents, with the wind whipping against the windows. A stray branch had torn through one side of our screened-in porch. When the sun finally rose, it could barely fight its way through the clouds. In the dim half-light the flooded streets and pools of drowned grass were slowly sucked into the air. The humidity climbed higher with every passing minute.

I woke up with my bedroom window wide open. My right arm hung over the edge of the mattress, a half smoked cigarette still clutched between my fingers. The floor was covered in ashes and butts that had missed the week-old Wendy's cup, half full of grimy water, that I'd repurposed into an ashtray. I fumbled around the bed until I found a lighter. I re-lit the cigarette. It tasted stale. I smoked it anyway.

I pulled off my sweat-soaked undershirt and tossed it on the floor. Kicking it around, I made a halfhearted effort to clean up the mess of ashes that had mixed with rainwater dripping from the window sill. I left the shirt on the floor and stumbled over to the bathroom. Even in the heat and humidity, I could feel the chills coming on.

I fumbled through the drawer. My morning ritual was always the same. Under a pile of empty baggies, I found my shining diamond: one small brown bag, half full, just enough to find the strength to get dressed and start my day. Still in a haze, I filled an old contact case with water from the sink. My body aching, I lowered myself to the floor and pressed my back up against the wall. I reached into the cabinet under the sink, grabbing from a pile of orange-capped rigs. The numbers had long since faded away.

I went through them in turn, finally settling on one that seemed suitable enough; it couldn't have been used more than five or six times. The ritual was the same as always, and when I'd registered and let the belt drop from my teeth, I felt warmth spread through my body. It wasn't enough, not to get what I really wanted, but the chills were gone in an instant all the same.

I breathed a sigh of relief and rose to my feet a new man, ready to meet the morning. "Bring on the brightness." I dabbed at my arm with a piece of toilet paper and tossed it aside. Immediately, I sought out my phone in the mess of blankets piled atop my bed. I dialed, waiting impatiently as it rang. I could've sworn it rang for hours before I finally heard a voice on the other end.

"Yeah?"

"I need."

"When?"

"Soon as I figure out my cash situation. Maybe an hour."

"Same spot. Lemme know when you're ten minutes away." The phone clicked silent.

Satisfied, I scanned the floor for a cigarette with enough left on it for a puff. I smoked two or three butts, tossed them into the cup, and stumbled out into the kitchen. Outside my window, the morning sun still struggled to break through the clouds.

I opened the fridge. It was empty, as always. From the other side of the room, I could hear T snoring on the couch. I turned on the faucet and tilted my head to drink from it. Back in my room, I counted coins and emptied my wallet, all to a grand total of eleven dollars. Just enough.

In seconds, I was in the car, still wearing the same stained clothes I'd left sitting on the floor all week. I stopped at the gas station. Cigarettes were out of the question. Ruefully, I spent eighty-three cents on a black and mild. I smoked half of it as I cruised south on the highway. The other half would be for after.

I picked up my phone and dialed.

"Yeah?"

"Almost there."

"How many?"

"Just one."

There was a pause. "Seriously? You're getting me up in the morning for just one?"

"I'll be back later."

"Then just do it all now. Or do it all later. Just one?"

At that moment, I don't think I could've cared less about how annoyed he seemed. Hell, he hadn't hung up the phone. "I need this one. I gotta get some cash together. I can't deal with that shit when I'm sick."

"Fine. Five minutes."

I pulled my car off into the parking lot and leaned back. Deep inside my stomach, I could feel the anticipation welling up. Five minutes passed like an eternity. I fiddled with my rigs, readied my gear. I rubbed down my arms as best I could. I picked a spot, right there on my left arm. It was a good-looking spot.

The car pulled up next to me. I was out the door and back inside in moments. I had fifteen cents left in my pocket, but there was a smile on my face. I fixed up, lit the second half of my black and mild, and leaned back in my seat. I exhaled deeply and rubbed at my arm with a dirty fast-food napkin. I tossed it onto the floorboard.

I turned on the radio and savored every breath of smoke. I felt pleasantly warm and satisfied. I mouthed the words to the music and smoked the tiny cigar down to its plastic filter. When I had finished, I let my eyes flutter closed and reveled in the waves washing over my body. I drifted in and out of sleep for twenty or thirty minutes.

My phone rang. "What's up, T?"

"Where you at, brother?"

"Hollywood."

"You good?"

"Yeah," I said. "I'm pretty great. I scrounged up enough change for one and a black and mild. Beautiful way to start the day." I wiped a speck of dried blood from my arm.

"I feel ya'," he answered. "He got any of that other stuff?"

"Probably. I didn't ask. Had to do what I had to do, first. Didn't feel like bein' sick today."

"Can we go back?"

"Yeah, you know I gotta go back later anyway. One ain't gonna get me through the day."

"When?" He asked.

"Dunno," I said. "Whenever I find some money. I might have something I can pawn, I dunno, bro."

"Man." I could hear the change in his voice. "Don't pawn your stuff. I hate that, man. It's depressing."

"Less depressing than being puking sick."

"I got you," T answered. "You make sure he has my kind, and I'll float for some of yours."

"You sure?" I already had the car in drive.

"Yeah, bro. Don't pawn your stuff."

"Thanks," I said. I was speeding down the highway. "Lemme make the call." I hung up.

Half an hour later we were back. And then we were gone, floating back home on top of the world. We stopped and T bought me a pack of cigarettes.

As soon as we walked in the door, I gathered my kit and sat down on the couch. "You mind if I do it up here?"

"Nah," he said. "Do what you gotta do. But hey, don't leave those bloody paper towels on the table."

"Right, bro, of course." I smiled and set to work preparing my bounty. After a minute, I looked back up. "Hey, T?"

"Yeah, brother?" He'd already gotten started. T's methods were quicker than mine. He set his house key down on the table.

"You mind if I grab a pinch of that? Wanna throw it in here, get it all together, ya' know?"

"Yeah, bro." He grinned. "It was your gas and your guy. I can get ya' a pinch or two. What's mine is yours, brother."

"Thanks, T." I had everything into my system in the blink of an eye. For the next two hours, we sat on the coach smoking and bullshitting and laughing the day away. We ignored the filthy dishes in the sink, already circled by gnats. We ignored the dirty clothes strewn across the floor. We ignored the smell of cigarette smoke that had begun to seep into the walls and furniture. We ignored everything.

The world was shut outside. We didn't worry about money or our wreck of an apartment. We didn't worry about the upcoming work week. We didn't worry about our filthy clothes or greasy hair. We didn't worry about a single thing. We locked ourselves away into that black hole that we lived in. Tomorrow, even tonight, we would worry. But not now.

19

"**B**ear!" T's voice was quivering.

I was frozen. "Am I just supposed to stand still or what?"

"I don't think so. It's not a T-Rex."

"I don't think I'm supposed to run." I could barely screech out the words.

"Just keep walking. Nice and slow." T backpedaled as he spoke, taking quick glances over his shoulder to plot his course. "Just follow me."

I took a few precarious steps forward. "Is it coming this way?"

"I don't know," he said. "No. Maybe?"

I kept walking, taking each step with less confidence than the last. My legs trembled as my feet hit the ground.

Behind me, the crashing of branches sounded out once again from the edge of the clearing, followed by heavy footsteps. They were slow, plodding. And then, they stopped.

"What's it doing?" It took all my focus to continue walking.

"I don't know," T said. "It's just standing there looking around."

"How far out is it?"

"Just a couple of feet from the trees. It's just... standing there."

"Does it see us?"

"Pretty sure it does."

"Does it look pissed off?" It was all I could think to say.

"No? I don't know. It looks like a big bear." T shook his head. The path that ran along the edge of the cliff was only ten yards behind him, now. Just a few feet up the path, it took a sharp turn around the rising peak. The turn would hide us behind the trees. "What the hell do we do when we get up the path?"

"Let's just get around that curve," I said. "If it's not following us then, we can move up the path without making too much noise. I think."

"And if it's following us?" He asked.

"Like hell I know," I said.

"Should we have a backup plan?"

"I dunno," I answered. "Climb a tree? I've never run from a bear before."

By that point, we were just a few feet from the edge of the path. The bear hadn't moved. It was considering us, standing with its head cocked curiously to the side. It watched every single step we took.

T made it to the path first. He turned sideways, keeping one eye on the hulking creature staring at us from less than a football field away.

I heard the snap of twigs just as I reached the path and carefully made the turn. The bear was walking with slow, lumbering steps. It moved a few feet and stopped. Once again, it fixed its gaze on us. It took another step.

"Just keep walking," I said. I was just a few feet behind T. We made our way up the path deliberately. We fought to keep our eyes focused straight ahead, but they kept drifting backwards towards the clearing.

"It's not moving that fast," T said. "I think we're going faster than it is. I think we can get around this bend."

97

"Yeah," I said. "I just hope it loses interest once we're out of sight. The extent of my bear knowledge consists of 'Don't mess with them.'"

"You and me both, brother."

Behind us the steady footsteps of the bear continued unabated. It would slow and stop, then take a few quick steps forward. It was heading in our direction.

"I don't think we're gaining any ground," he said.

"I can't tell." The bend in the path was only a few feet away. It was starting the make me nervous. We would be temporarily out of sight, but so would the bear. If it came quickly around the bend, we wouldn't know until it was almost on us.

"We need more of a plan." T quickened his pace, just slightly. "It's following us."

"I..." My voice faltered. "T, I don't know. Let's just get around the bend. We'll still be able to hear it."

"Right," T answered. "Right."

The bear plodded on behind us. It stopped, sniffed at a tree, and continued along its path. Despite seeming to show no particular interest in us, there was absolutely no doubt we were being followed. The trees and flowers were only momentary distractions.

I tried to focus on my breathing. I tried to focus on anything but the steady footsteps pounding behind me. Deep breath in, deep breath out. Deep breath in, deep breath out. We came to the bend in the path. I glanced once more over my shoulder and made the turn. Instantly, the shadow of the trees fell upon my back. Behind us, the footsteps were coming as steady as ever. I quickened my pace.

"I know we said we're not supposed to run," T said. "But I really think maybe we should run."

"Not yet," I said. "Just keep speeding up a little at a time. Let's see how much distance we can get between us."

We were now making a steady uphill climb. Not far up ahead, the path took another sharp turn along the treeline. "Look," T said. He pointed ahead. "Maybe if we get to that bend before it gets to that first bend, we can lose it."

"Yeah," I said. "Yeah, okay." We walked faster, despite the constantly steepening ground beneath us. The weight of our packs increased with each step.

We were almost at the next bend when the sound behind us changed. In seconds, it was faster and harder than before. Over my shoulder, I could see the bear breaking into a light trot. Involuntarily, we both began to jog. Then to run. The bear increased its speed.

"Hell," T muttered.

"That says it pretty well," I answered.

"We need another plan."

"I know." I looked back behind us. The bear still appeared to move almost lazily, but it was gaining ground on us. Its mouth was wide open. Even at a distance, I could see its teeth. All I could see was its teeth.

We hit the bend in the path. Almost immediately, it narrowed and rose sharply up hill. Trees hung heavy over the left side of the path. On the opposite side was a sheer drop. Gravel slipped beneath our feet, bouncing downwards behind us.

The bear was closer.

"We can't run from it up this hill," T said. "We gotta try something."

"There's not a lot of options," I panted. "It's either down the cliff or up a tree."

"Yeah," he answered.

We turned sharply, crashing into the underbrush alongside the path. Heavy footsteps pounded along behind us.

I grabbed onto the first tree I could find that looked as if it could be climbed. Just as I pulled myself up onto the lowest branch, I heard the bear bursting into the woods. I grasped at the next branch, ignoring the burning in my fingers and hoisting myself upwards with every ounce of strength I could muster. I swung my legs around, planted them against the side of the tree, and scurried upwards as fast as I could.

Below, T was still running. He glanced side to side, searching for a branch low enough to grab onto. The bear pushed past my tree. It headed straight for him. T moved out of my view, leaving me with only the sound of his furious running, and the footsteps of the bear beating like a bass drum behind him. I heard the bear roar and the shaking of trees. The sound frightened me deep down in my core.

I heard the bear continuing to trample through the trees. Slowly, the sound faded into the distance. I waited, clinging desperately onto the tree branch.

The sound of the rampaging bear disappeared. The mountain was silent.

"T?" I heard my voice ringing off of the trees. "T?"

No answer came.

I would've heard it if it got him. I lowered myself down the side of the tree. I planted my feet firmly on the forest floor and looked over my surroundings. The path was just visible. A deep trail ran along the ground where the bear had trampled the ground beneath it. I followed the trail, still listening intently for any sound in the distance. "T!" I didn't want to call too loud. The bear was, presumably, still somewhere not far out of earshot.

I shook my head. Again, I could feel anxiety tearing at my skin. My breathing was heavy. "T!" Silence. "T!" Louder this time. I walked along the bear's trail of destruction.

I scanned the surrounding trees. There were no signs of any struggle. There was no sign of T at all. "T!"

"Over here, brother!" His voice sounded weak.

I turned to the side. He was sitting on the lower limb of a tree, just off the trampled trail. His clothes were ripped. Blood stained his shirt.

"T!" I rushed towards him.

"I'm fine," he said. Gingerly, he lowered himself out of the tree. "Bear didn't get me. Just tore myself up pretty good trying to get up that tree."

I laughed. Despite everything, I laughed. It overtook me. I leaned against a tree, panting, as laughter spewed uncontrollably from my mouth.

"I'm glad you think it's so freaking funny."

"T." I was gasping for breath, struggling to control my laughter. "T, I thought you were freaking done. I saw your bloody shirt and figured that bear got you and that was the freakin' end of that."

T laughed. "Nah, brother." He reached up, pulling his pack down from the lowest tree branch. "Feelin' a little rough, but I'm in one piece."

I clapped him on the back. In silence, we made our way back to the path. As the adrenaline faded away, I was overcome with a vibrant joy. The sun suddenly seemed brighter. The leaves were greener. The air was sweet. Once again, the mountain had thrown everything it had at us. And once again, we were back on the path.

20

We found ourselves back at the clearing, backs pressed against the trees. The adrenaline had faded away into exhaustion. We sat in silence, our heavy breathing slowly fading into a rhythmic, meditation-like pace. I smoked a cigarette, slower than usual, taking care to taste each breath of smoke as I exhaled.

"Well," T said. "That was somethin', wasn't it?"

"Yeah," I answered. "It sure was."

"You know," he said. "After all the years, all the dumb stuff we've done, I think that's the only time it's ever involved being chased by a wild animal."

"I dunno." I shrugged. "I seem to remember once, back in Florida, when my cat gave you a pretty darn good run for your money. I've never seen you dive over a couch quite like that."

"Dude," T answered. "That cat, she had murder in her eyes. I swear, man, I just woke up and she was staring at me. She was gonna take me out in my sleep. I could feel it." He laughed. "Murder in her eyes, bro. I swear."

I smiled. "She was a good cat."

"To you, maybe."

"You did look pretty damn scared when you woke up."

"She was like a foot from my face!" T answered. "I'm tellin' ya', she was just watching me, waiting for me to open my eyes so she could tear 'em out."

"All two hundred whatever pounds of you, scared to hell by a two-pound cat."

"I'd rather do the bear thing again than piss that cat off. Honestly."

I laughed, recalling the image of T waking up from a nap with terror in his eyes, screaming in fright while he launched himself over the back of the living room couch. My little cat, perched on the coffee table with a curious expression on her face, just stared and wandered silently into the back room. T lay behind the couch for a solid ten minutes, huffing and puffing and babbling on and on about how the cat wanted him gone.

"You remember that time," he asked. "When I accidentally shut the cat in the bathroom? She didn't meow, she didn't do a darn thing. She just waited there, for hours probably, until I opened the door again, then launched herself at me."

"She tore up your feet pretty damn good." I smiled at the memory.

"Scarier than the bear, I'm tellin' ya." T glanced around. He eyed the woods, searching the trees carefully. "Speakin' of which, it's probably about time we got moving. We wasted a lot of daylight."

"I wouldn't call surviving a bear a waste."

T shrugged and started walking. We walked in silence for a half mile or so. We pretended to enjoy the scenery, to take in the view. Privately, we were both scanning the forest for anything bigger than a squirrel. We stopped more than a few times at any hint of a noise, holding our breath and waiting. When we were satisfied it was nothing, we moved on, stepping lightly and looking in every direction except forward. The path steepened steadily, continuing to wind itself around the side of the mountain.

"We're really goin' up, at this point," T commented. "I wonder how much further we gotta go?"

"No idea," I said. "Figure we keep going up while we can. We've only got a few hours of daylight left. We can set up camp a little early today, at the first nice spot we find, and use what's left of the sun to really look over these maps, figure out exactly where we're at. All a' that stuff."

"Sure," T said. "You know what I'm ready for, bro?"

"What's that?"

"A meal, a real honest-to-goodness meal. Or at least, the best attempt we can make at it. I say tonight, we get a solid fire going and really eat. We brought more than enough food, and after today, we darn well deserve it."

"Not gonna argue with that," I said. I lit another cigarette and gazed upward at the path. I could already feel the ache in my legs. Running from a bear certainly hadn't been in my plans, and it reminded me that I wasn't in the same shape I'd been in when we last tried to climb Grandfather, a decade earlier. "You startin' to get as tired as I am?"

"Nah." T shook his head. "I feel good, man. I feel light. I don't get exhausted these days. Not anymore. You need to stop and take a rest?"

"Just for a minute." I lit a cigarette and sat down on a rock. The path had turned inward, and for the moment, we weren't standing on the edge of a cliff. Trees hung overhead, casting shadows that deepened as the day went on.

"I'm glad we did this," T said. "After everything, it's pretty awesome that we're back up here."

"Me too, brother," I replied. "I mean, after last time, I always figured we'd try again. But then, ya' know, time went on. Things got... " I paused. "Well, hell, T, you know

104

how things got. Honestly, I didn't think I'd ever see the mountains again, much less get another shot at this climb."

"I hear ya'."

"Hell," I said. "For a while there, I didn't think I'd get a second chance at anything. It all felt pretty damn permanent, you know? That's just how things were gonna be. I didn't see an end to any of it."

"So don't waste it." His voice took on a somber tone. A serious expression adorned his face. "Just like everything else, man, this is a second chance. Some people... some people don't get second chances, ya' know? Hell, a lot of people don't get second chances." He shook his head. "A lot of us don't get second chances."

"I shouldn't have needed a second chance." I looked down at my feet. For a moment, I watched the cherry embers creep down my cigarette, devouring it in slow, methodical silence.

"Brother," T said. "Let's not do all this again. What's done is done."

"Wasted damn near a third of my life in that black hole." I was still watching my cigarette.

"Well," he answered. "When you live to be eighty or ninety, and it's all some distant memory, it won't be a third of your life then. It'll be a few years that you learned a helluva lotta things from, in the end."

"Yeah," I said. "Yeah, T. It wasn't just me, though, you know, suffering for my mistakes."

"I know," he said. "But come on, let's not do this again. We're lookin' forward now, remember?" He turned his gaze upwards. "There's one failure you can atone for, right here right now, something physical and concrete and measurable. Whatever the hell else you want to go away, it's all one step at a time. And right now, one foot in front of the other, we're going to step all the way up this mountain and tie the goddamn score."

I nodded and stood up. "I guess every time we get into this, we go in circles, don't we?"

He shrugged. "You need to talk. You need to talk. A lot's happened, man... A lotta things went really wrong. It's not like you're gonna bring it up once and then we're gonna solve it all, and you're gonna put it behind you and go on all bright and chipper. It's not all gonna just go away at once and leave you with some damn transcendent sparkling vision of 'Everything's okay now.' It just doesn't happen like that. You know it, too, as well as I do."

"I know," I said. "But some things are harder to live with than others. I wonder, sometimes, if some of them will ever go away at all."

"If they don't," he said. "Then they don't. But there's too much ahead to let the past beat you. If it never goes away, then you learn to deal with it, and figure it'll be easier one day. And if it doesn't get easier? Well, then, deal with it all anyway. If that's your burden to bear, then that's your burden to bear. You can handle it."

"You're right, T," I said. "Of course, you're right. Sometimes, ya' know, I feel like I really got it. I feel like I have a handle on myself and everything that's happened, and then other times it just all seems so goddamn big and hopeless and crushing and... hell, I dunno."

"You do have this," T said. "Maybe you don't see it, but everyone else around you can. I won't say you're different. Hell, I'd say you're more like the you I always knew than you have been for a long time. But I can see it in your eyes, I can hear it in your voice. I can tell the difference between this time and every half-assed attempt you made before. You got your soul back, my brother."

My eyes were damp. "I don't know if my soul was worth the price, T. I mean, when it…, when you…"

"Brother," he said. climb doesn't have to be like it was before." Again, he pointed up at the face of Grandfather. "This whole thing, it's not going to break you. And him, up there, he's not going to beat you. He's not going to beat us. Not again."

"Yeah, T." I stood up, turning my gaze to the face staring down at us. I stamped out my cigarette. "You're right, again. This time around, everything is different."

21

It was over a decade earlier that T and I had first attempted to climb Grandfather. After a day of rest, we threw together a haphazard collection of everything we thought we'd need and filled up two backpacks that were still lying around from our early days of high school. They were in poor shape and weighed heavily on our backs.

We dashed up the mountain with untouchable confidence. Young and riding a cascading wave of independence, we bounded up the slopes with less forethought than we gave to planning a Friday night party. We found success quickly, hopping along logs and stones to cross rivers and scrambling up cliffs through sheer force of will alone. The first night we made it nearly half-way up, hiking through the day and on into the night. When we finally set up camp, the stars were shining high overhead. We collected logs by the pale light of the moon, and ate our fill next to a roaring fire. We filled our canteens from a nearby stream, guzzling down the icy water flowing along the rocks. We stayed up late, drinking whiskey from a flask and musing over what the next day would bring. The embers of the fire died off long before the conversation, and only when the whiskey was nearly exhausted did we fall off into an uncomfortable sleep, nestled between the rocks in sleeping bags, beneath the light of the stars.

I awoke early, just as the sun was beginning to peek through the morning mists that had descended upon the mountains. My clothes were damp with dew. My back ached. There was a dull pounding in my head. My stomach rumbled, but not with hunger. "Hey, T, you up?"

"Sorta," he answered. "I've been waking up on and off all night. I don't feel so good, bro."

"I know," I said. "Neither do I."

"It's not a hangover," T said. "But man, there's something not good happenin' to my insides." Before I could answer, he was up and dashing for the woods. He relieved himself violently behind a tree.

It was only moments before I was dashing the opposite direction to do the same. We hadn't thought twice of drinking from the streams flowing down the mountain, and in fact had continued to do so in an effort to prevent the dehydration we could already feel setting in. The condition that those familiar with the Appalachian Trail referred to as "Trekker's Trots" was then wholly unknown to us.

The pounding in my head was growing worse as I leaned up against a tree and smoked. "T," I called. "How're you feelin' over there?"

"Like shit. You?"

"Yeah. Literally."

T laughed, halfheartedly, as he made his way back to the middle of the small clearing we'd set up camp in. He sat down on a rock and surveyed his surroundings. "Well, what the hell you wanna do?"

I shrugged. "Don't feel like a little headache and a case of the runs should keep us from finishing the climb. We can't be that far from the peak." A map was another on the long list of items we'd forgotten to include in our packing.

"Yeah," T answered. "I agree. We can hit the peak, hang out up there for a bit, and then get back to the car before too late. Going back is downhill, so I'm sure we can do it in half a day or so."

"Of course," I said. "Going back will be easy." We still had no idea, then, just the misery that we'd gotten ourselves into. Physical maladies aside, youth and hubris still guided our thinking. We would assault the peak, down the last of the whiskey at the summit, and casually trot back down the mountain in time to enjoy dinner at home. Nothing to it.

We set off at a brisk pace, laughing and joking despite our discomfort. As we climbed, the sun rose higher and burned hotter. The mists descended below us and vaporized into the air. Our socks and underwear were soaked through with sweat and humidity. My feet begin to burn as the way grew narrower and rockier. We stopped, repeatedly, to drink from the stream that zigzagged back and forth across the path. We stopped just as many times to relieve ourselves in the woods, doing so with increasing frequency as the day went on. As the hours passed we grew silent, trudging with slow, measured steps up the ever-steepening path.

When T spoke, I swore it had been hours since I'd heard his voice break the drudgery of our determined march. "Brother, I really don't feel so good."

"I know," I said. "But hey, we passed a sign pointing towards Attic Window the last time we crossed another trail. It can't be that much further."

"No," he replied. He stopped and crouched down, reaching out to steady himself against a tree. "My vision's blurring. I don't feel right." He took a sip from his canteen.

I sat down, pushing my back to a rock for support. I nearly lost my balance as I tried to lower myself to the ground. "You okay, T?"

"Don't know." He didn't look up at me. Sweat was pouring down his face. "I feel really bad, man. Can I have some water?"

I passed him my canteen. His was already empty. I tried to smoke a cigarette, but the smoke burned my throat. It tasted dry and rough in my mouth. I took a sip of whiskey. Instantly, I felt worse. Neither of us wanted to be the one to say it, but we both knew we were in no shape to keep climbing. I could feel the specter of failure looming above us, cackling wildly. "It can't be much further."

"It can't be much further," T repeated. He grasped at the tree behind him and dragged himself to his feet. The effort exhausted him and he leaned forward and vomited.

I stumbled forward, ignoring the dull pain that had began to radiate through my body. I heard T follow behind me. It was only a few hundred yards before we could hear the stream gurgling ahead of us. Summoning all of our strength, we quickened our pace until we reached the cool water. I drank deep, filled my canteen, and drank again. I lay down on my back next to the water and closed my eyes, drawing in deep breath after deep breath. The pounding in my head didn't subside.

"If we collapse up here," T said. "Nobody's gonna find us. Nobody knows we're here. We'll die up here."

"No," I said, my eyes still closed. "We've got water right here. We ate a big dinner. We could make it a long time, if we had to. Somebody would find us."

"We're going to die up here." T's voice was heavy with defeat.

"We have to get up."

"I can't."

I opened my eyes and rolled over onto my stomach. Gingerly, I pulled myself into a crouching position. My stomach rumbled. "It's coming again." It took all the energy I had to crawl into the woods.

When I crawled back out, T was standing up, gazing with unfocused eyes back down the way we had come. His face was blank. He swayed back and forth, barely maintaining his balance. Without a word, he took a step forward, and then another.

I followed after him. We were silent, save for the steady plodding sound of our footsteps. I didn't bother trying to smoke. I turned to gaze back at the face of Grandfather above us. It seemed almost jovial, reveling in our defeat. My soul felt destroyed as the realities of our failure convened upon my heart. Each step was another in a series of defeats. As we made our way back down the mountainside, the despair deep within my stomach grew into a gnawing pit. It ate at me from the inside.

T stopped to vomit and then continued walking with tiny, deliberate steps. He stumbled and fell. Without a word, he rose to his feet and cast aside his backpack.

I followed suit. Every extra pound was a burden we couldn't afford to bear. The burden weighing upon our minds and hearts was darker and heavier than the weight of the packs. As the sun slipped beneath the horizon, we marched on in silence. I didn't look back again. I couldn't bear to meet the sneering gaze of the face on the mountain.

After what felt like hours, T spoke. His voice was hoarse and raspy. "We failed, my brother."

"Yeah." It was all I could think of to say. The feeling in my stomach hurt worse than the aches of dehydration that racked my body. I was barely even sweating anymore.

Darkness closed in upon us. We rested every few minutes. We followed the path that twisted and turned down the side of the mountain. The moon rose high in victory, bathing the peaks at our backs in a pale, ghostly illumination. It gloated alongside Grandfather. We didn't have to speak to know that we both felt the same, helpless and defeated.

"One day," I said. "We'll do it again."

"Yeah, we will." At that point, T didn't mean it any more than I did. Our grand adventure had ended in failure. We had pushed ourselves against the forces of nature, and we had lost, bitterly and completely. Our dreams had vanished with the last sunlight, and we were only two lonesome, insignificant insects inching down the side of a grand testament to the unconquerable strength of a world in which we were unable to assert our place. We shambled on in shame and darkness, returning to our world empty and defeated. The feeling would stay with us long after we stumbled out of the forest. It remained there, deep inside our souls, gnawing away at us. In my dreams, the face of Grandfather leered down at me, and I cowered below, wondering at those times if it was really true that, as Hemingway said, "A man can be destroyed. but not defeated," for I felt then that defeat had struck deep into the very heart of my being and devoured me from the inside out, leaving behind only empty skin and broken dreams.

22

"**I** think we're higher up than we made it last time," T speculated as we stopped by the side of the trail. In front of us, a mess of fallen branches had complicated the path.

"Probably," I answered. I glanced around the woods, hoping in vain to find some landmark that I could tie to our last attempt a decade previously. Nothing looked familiar. "We passed that stream a little ways back. I think that was our high water mark."

T grinned. "All unknown from here then, huh?" He pulled himself up onto the top of the pile of debris left by the storm. "Looks like this really is the end of easy walkin'. It's about to get really steep, really fast."

"Yeah?" I scrambled through the brush to get a better view. The trail rose sharply before us.

"You think we're ready for this?"

I shrugged. "Haven't thrown up today, so I figure we're at least a step ahead of last time."

He laughed. "Still plenty of time left for that, brother."

"Nah," I said. "Not this time. I'll be darned if Grandfather's gonna beat me again. This is it, buddy. There's no going back." I glanced up at the path ahead.

"This is it," he agreed.

Even as we turned our heads upward, the dense cover of clouds began to draw away. The sun, suddenly brilliant and radiating, burst through the gray of the sky.

Rays of light glittered along the treetops, dancing across the horizon as the entirety of the mountain unfolded in front of us. Light reflected off of the leaves remaining on the trees, refracting in a prism of exploding color. The face of Grandfather rose up clear before us, his eyes wide and focused, staring down the sharp peak of his nose and focusing upon the two of us, standing there exposed on the side of the mountain. The warmth built up inside me even before I felt it on my skin, spanning outwards and spreading through my limbs. He was right above us, now.

I blinked, twice, and turned my gaze back towards the path. In silent agreement, we walked on. Our boots crunched against the fallen leaves and snapped twigs scattered across the wet path. Walking was slow along the saturated ground.

"This is great!" T's outburst was suddenly triumphant and joyous, his voice booming against the distant peaks and echoing throughout the valleys. "Brother," he said. "This is it, don't you see? We're gonna make it this time! I can feel it, man. I can feel it in every inch of my body. Grandfather, he's afraid."

His words brought truth to the view in front of me. The rain had failed to defeat us; the clouds had cast aside their arms and bowed to our march. The path before us was laid bare, bathed in a golden glow. Destiny, fate, whatever we wanted to call it, was all coming together as, one step at a time, we fought our way up the mountainside. All obstacles fell to the side before our furious march.

My mind wandered. The enormity of it all was finally beginning to descend upon me; the momentous scope of our journey filled every crevice of my mind. My first instinct was, somehow, to be depressed. I thought of our past failure. I thought of all my own past failures. I thought of every moment T and I had shared that had led to this one final journey. I thought of everything I'd done, of everyone I'd hurt, of every mistake I'd ever made in my life. Every instinct told me to let it all in, to know it was all real, to let the enormity of it all overcome me and know that no simple journey to the summit of a mountain would ever erase all the shame and guilt that I'd accumulated throughout my life.

For once, though, my conscious mind prevailed against my instinct, and the depression washed away like grains of sand beneath a cool wave. The weight of the world seemed lighter, even as the weight of my steps grew heavier. I felt, really felt, the sun on my back and the breeze on my face. I saw the green in every leaf. I saw the brilliant blue of the sky. I saw the absolute majesty of Grandfather's face above me, and standing there beneath his glare, my feelings of enmity faded away. I wasn't staring down an enemy, no, but a harshly fair mentor challenging me, pushing me, demanding of me that I conquer him. He offered to me his own defeat, his own damnation, dangling it in front of me, knowing that in his destruction I could find salvation.

T felt it, too. I could tell in the way he raised his eyes up to meet the challenge before him, no longer staring in exhaustion at the path below his feet. His steps were stronger, more deliberate. We were marching, side by side, towards the redemption that we sought. Our enemy wasn't Grandfather Mountain. It never had been. It wasn't ourselves, either; that was the easy answer. The enemy was everything we had accumulated—not just the negative, but the positive, too, because in our minds the positive was only there to remind us of what we'd never have again. The enemy was within our own minds, that nagging feeling that nothing mattered and mistakes couldn't be unmade and every decision we'd ever made had been wrong. It couldn't be true, though, not now, because those decisions had led us here, to climbing the side of The Mountain, to rising higher than we ever had before. In that one moment, we lived a thousand lives, sitting there in the present and soaking in every bit of energy that the universe had to offer, putting it back out tenfold with positive energy and joy and the unassailable assertion that some day, somehow, everything would eventually be okay because we had the power within ourselves to make it okay. The mountain was the lens through which we would refocus our lives.

"Do you feel it?" T asked.

"I think I do, brother." I stopped, for just a moment, to take in the scenery. I breathed in deep. "The whole world, our whole world, it's up here, ya' know?"

"It is," he answered. "This is all that's left. Just you, and me, and our old buddy Grandfather."

"Me and you and Grandfather," I said. "That's right. That's all there is right now. Just this one present moment."

"Right now," T said. "But it leads to more, my friend. This is the path to everything! This is the answer. This is our truth! I feel it, man, so deep in my soul, I feel it. This might be the only right thing we've ever done but it's the rightest thing in the whole dismal world, and it makes up for everything else we never said or did while we had the chance. I feel like we're up here to save our souls."

"We're up here because the only place we could be is here. There's no other place, nothing else to do. That's it, right? I mean, there's just this moment, and we're here, so this has to be all there is to do because it's what we're doing right now."

"And everything is right with the universe." T laughed.

"Everything is right with the universe," I repeated.

"And it always will be."

"You think so?"

T shrugged. "Hell, man, everything's gonna be as it should. I don't see what else it can be other than exactly how it's supposed to be."

"I'm not sure if that's comforting or depressing."

"Hell if I know," he said. "Both? Neither? I guess both. There's shades of it in everything. That's how truth usually works, my friend. It's never as absolute as you'd expect it to be. It's just how it is, ya' know?"

"Yeah," I said. "Yeah."

"Everything," T repeated. "Is gonna be everything."

We continued walking.

The Ranch   23

I sat in a small office with wood-paneled walls and a peeling floor. A white floor fan whirred softly in the corner, pivoting back and forth. I was in an armless chair, leaning back, with my left leg crossed over my thigh, forming a lap.

"Well," said Margot, watching me from across the desk. "It's been two weeks, now. How are you feeling?"

"Like there's no way it's been that long." I shook my head and laughed. "To be honest, I'm not sure if all of this is real, sometimes. I'm not sure if I'm gonna wake up in Florida in a mass of sweaty sheets fumbling for my phone. A lot of times, I like to pretend that I'll wake up before that. This is a dream within a nightmare, and none of it ever happened. None of any of it, I mean."

"That's understandable." She nodded. "But you also know that's not the way it is. This is very real, and everything before this was real. This is where you are, in the present moment. So, tell me, how are you feeling?"

"Less lousy than most days?" I replied. "I dunno,Margot. I'm still not so sure of it all. I want to be, don't get me wrong. But it's not the same in here. It's easy in here. Everything makes sense when the world is only a few acres wide, ya' know?"

"Of course." She shifted in her chair. She'd abandoned the use of a notepad, after our first few individual settings. That made it easier. It felt more like a conversation than an interrogation. "But you're not going to be here forever. It's halfway, now. You have to start

119

thinking about what you're going to do after. Do you have a plan? Or a plan to make a plan?"

"Not a damned thing," I said. "I've considered applying to NASA, or maybe going on an Antarctic expedition. Ya' know, study some penguins and all. Sounds like a good time."

She smiled at me. "You have to start thinking about it, sooner rather than later. We're in the moment now, but we're not sitting still. I promise you, the second half is going to go by a lot faster than the first did."

"I dunno, that first week and all those meds, it went by pretty quick."

"I don't think I saw you smile for that entire first week, either," she responded. "You know, you've been doing really well. You're a completely different person than you were two weeks ago."

"I dunno if that's good or bad," I said. "I mean, Margot, am I still me? I don't know what to think sometimes. I'm not the same person from one minute to the next. One second, I'm in the moment and appreciating this chance I have, and the next I'm lamenting the fact that I'm unlucky enough to have to wake up every morning after all I've done. And..." I lowered my head. "I feel bad, not just about me, but about everyone else. I haven't been a good person for the last few years, ya' know."

"I don't believe that for a second," she said. "You've been a sick person. That's different."

"So I wasn't responsible for my own actions? Because they were some pretty lousy actions."

"I think," Margot replied. "That you're doing your best to take responsibility for those actions. And you're trying to get better. I'm not going to lie and say you can erase all that. You know I wouldn't try to lie to you. But you can be the best version of yourself—and still be you. And for everyone out there who loves you, or ever did love you, that's an amazing thing. You don't exist in a void. If you give up now, regardless of what you feel like you've done, you give up on all those people. Do they deserve to be given up on, after all the love and support they've given you?"

"Oh, come on, Margot, it's not like…"

"Do they, or do they not, deserve to be given up on?"

I sighed. "They don't. They don't."

"Well," she said. "Then it looks like you need to stop playing the victim, pitying yourself, and start figuring out what you can do when you get out of here to be the best person you can be for those people. And for yourself. Because you are worth something, as hard as you beat yourself up. I know it, and I think you know it, too."

"I dunno, I just…"

"No bull!" She snapped. "Just stop. When you first arrived here, you made a promise. You promised me that if I did everything I could to help you, you would do everything you could to help yourself."

"You're right," I said. "I did. You're right."

"Good. I've kept my end of the bargain, right?"

I felt tears welling up in my eyes. I nodded, even as I was turning my head down to conceal the dampness running down my cheeks. "You have, Margot. You've done more for me than anyone here. I probably would've given up by now if not for you."

"You're doing it again!" Her voice rose sharply. "This isn't about me. This is about you. You've done this. And when you leave here, you'll be the one in charge. I can't make your decisions for you. I know how strong you are. I believe in you. And you've got to believe in yourself, if you want to make it out there."

"I don't know if just believing in myself is enough."

"It isn't," she said. "That's why you're here today. We're working on your plan, on figuring out a way to make sure that you can live a long, healthy, happy life and never have to end up at a place like this again."

"You know what I really want to do, M?"

"What's that?"

"I don't know if you remember, but I talked about it in one of our groups. Hell, I probably mentioned it several times. About ten years ago, ol' T and I, we tried to climb Grandfather Mountain out in North Carolina...on a whim. We damn near made it, too, but we were young and stupid."

"Of course," she said. "I remember that. It sounded like quite the memory. What about it?"

I smiled, wide across my face the way T had always smiled. "I want to go back, Margot. And this time, it'll be different. I want to conquer the mountain."

24

Even as the terrain grew more challenging, I felt my mind wandering. T floated like a ghost in front of me, bounding up the mountainside as my thoughts sprawled endlessly across the expanse of the landscape. The ache in my legs had become unreal. The goal, in that moment, wasn't to reach the peak; it was only to take another step. Each step was possible, and in those simple victories, I felt my confidence begin to grow.

This task required no Herculean effort, only simple moments of mindful will. With every step, I conquered the moment. It became another in a series of moments that I could leave in the past. Each moment of pain was only that, a simple moment, and nothing that had happened before or would happen after mattered in the slightest. All that had been simply was, and all that would come was only imagination. Then and there, bathed in the sunlight on the side of a mountain, I existed in a state of singular focus.

"How you feelin', brother?" T's voice carried itself along the wind.

"Like all is right with the world!" I meant it, just then. I felt deep inside that I meant it, really and truly.

"That's because all is right with the world." He scrambled around a boulder, grabbing on to an overhanging tree limb and nimbly pulling himself further up the path. "I mean, really, that's the only way it can be, right?"

I shook my head and laughed. "Damn you and your overwhelming positivity." I followed just behind him, slipping past the boulder and pushing my way upwards.

"It's the only way to be, my brother! This is our life in the moment, and it's beautiful."

"Yeah," I said. "Yeah, T." Our voices fell silent as we climbed higher. I felt rocks slipping beneath my feet. I felt the wind whipping against my cheeks. I gazed upward and pushed with all my will against the mountain, and then I slipped. My left leg buckled, caught underneath me as I felt my ankle twist sharply.

All thoughts of the world and my life and our journey were pushed from my mind in a single, gasping breath. My vision took on a red tinge as I fell. My face hit hard against the ground, my breathless body tumbling backwards. I wasn't sure if I cried out or fell in silence, but in that moment my mind was overcome by an all-encompassing pain. I rolled three or four feet back down the slope, coming to a jarring stop against the same boulder I had leapt effortlessly around only seconds before.

"You okay?" T turned around, gliding back down the mountain towards where I lay crumpled on the ground.

"I..." Words meant nothing to me. My entire existence was comprised of my throbbing ankle. I said a few choice words ad I looked downward at my leg. Blood was pouring from a wide, long gash along my calf. It stained the soil beneath me a deep, dark color. Fragments of rock and dirt clung to the wound.

"Hey, you okay?" T repeated as he jogged towards me.

"My ... leg." Blinded by pain, I struggled to string a sentence together, blinded by pain.

T leaned over me, crouched down, and inspected my leg. "I'm gonna move your leg, just a little, so I can get a look at this, okay?"

"Yeah," I gasped. "Yeah, just do it." I grunted in pain as he rolled me onto my back and stretched out my leg. The blood flow was already beginning to slow down.

"Okay, bro, you got a nasty cut here," he said. "Good news is, it doesn't look too deep. It's just long and bloody."

"So you're saying I'm gonna die, right?"

"Without a doubt. I give it five, maybe ten minutes most. I'd recommend you go ahead and make peace with God while you have the chance."

I managed a short laugh, shaking my head. "It's not the cut. It's my ankle. I stepped down wrong and twisted it a rock."

"Okay," he said. "One thing at a time, right? I know you've got a first aid kit in your pack. Let's get this thing cleaned up, make sure the bleeding's stopped, and then we'll see what we can do about your ankle."

I spent the next fifteen minutes or so cleaning out the long gash along my leg and bandaging it to the best of my abilities with what meager supplies we had. Once it was fully wrapped, T stretched out a hand as I attempted to get back onto my feet. Just above the line of my boot, my ankle was already turning various shades of purple.

"Look, buddy," T said to me. "I'm not gonna lie to you, it doesn't exactly look pretty. You wanna try putting a little weight on it and see how that goes?"

"No, not really." I managed another laugh. "This living in the moment bit, it's a little bit less pleasant when the moment consists of throbbing pain."

"Well, make peace with that. It's all you can do," he said serenserenelyly. And then, added quickly, "Don't be a whiner."

"Shut up." I shook my head and steadied myself. I pushed down, gingerly, on the ankle. I felt a rush of pain, but remained upright. "I wouldn't say it feels pleasant, but I think I can stand on it."

"Good, good." T took a few steps, maneuvering himself so that he was standing downhill just behind me. "Try to take a few steps. If your clumsy body falls over, I'll see if I can catch you before you nail your leg on another rock ... unless you really feel like you want matching scars?"

I took several small, feeble steps. "I can walk." I gritted my teeth, wanting to yell out in pain, to swear loudly and sit back down. Instead, I felt a wave of determination wash over my body. My mind felt strangely clear. I knew the pain existed, but that was in another time and place. It was only my mind, in that instant, and in my mind the decision had already been made. "Let's go."

"Brother, be careful with this," T said. "The higher we go, the harder it's gonna be to get back down. Especially once we get to the ladders. Those aren't far ahead."

"Let's go," I repeated. I pushed forward. I wouldn't allow myself to consider giving up. The only options I had were to continue now, or to rest and hope, and I had no intention of trusting to a miraculous healing over the next few minutes. "Grandfather's not going to beat us again. Do you hear that?" I turned towards the peak, shouting into the wind. "You won't beat us again!"

"Okay then." T took another few steps forward. "You got this, or you need some help?"

"I have to do this on my own." Ignoring the pain, I resumed my slow hike up the mountainside. I was sure, by that point, that nothing was broken. I imagined the swelling would get worse, and that the journey to the peak would be immeasurably more difficult than I'd expected only minutes earlier, but there was no thought of quitting in my mind.

"You don't have to do anything on your own, my friend. One way or another, you know I'm here to help you get where you need to go." T patted me on the back. "Now, come on, let's do this. You take the lead, and set the pace. I'll try to stay behind you so you don't fall off the side of the damn mountain in case that old man ankle of yours doesn't hold up."

"Thanks, T." The hike leveled out over the next few minutes, then took a sudden steep turn upward. The bandage around my leg was soaked through with blood. After a few hundred yards, I stopped to spray antiseptic and wrap a new cloth around my wound. The bleeding had nearly stopped by this point. T was right. The wound was long and wide, but not deep. Purely superficial. It was nothing that would stop me from completing the journey I'd dreamed of for the last decade.

We laughed as we climbed, even as I struggled more with each passing minute. We sang old songs, loud and off-key, that reminded us of years before. We told the same stupid jokes we'd laughed at a hundred times. We reminisced about our high school days, about the stupid pranks and nearly forgotten friends. In the company of friendship and joy, I almost completely forgot about my ankle. I forgot about the aching in my legs and the burning in my lungs. Just as it had so many times along the climb, my body felt light with peace. T floated up the mountainside, and I followed dutifully after, eyes always looking towards the peak.

I was never one to believe the universe had a plan for me. I didn't believe in any cosmic karma that would ensure everything magically worked out. But I did believe, in that moment, that maybe everything had worked out exactly as it was supposed to. Everything had led me to this moment, to undertake this journey. I'd set out seeking some kind of redemption, thinking I could erase the past with one momentous journey culminating in a moment of ultimate triumph. Somewhere along the way, it had all changed. I wasn't seeking to erase the past any longer, nor was I looking to build a new future for myself. I was simply looking to exist, free of suffering, on exactly my own terms, not bound by anything that had come before or would after. Standing atop Grandfather would neither right past wrongs nor guarantee future happiness, but I knew, in that moment, that this journey was right.

I was exactly where I was supposed to be, doing exactly what I was supposed to do, and I concerned myself with nothing else. I felt the reality of being deep inside my soul as my mind opened itself up the endless possibilities of life. The happiness that overcame me, then and there, didn't come from the mountain or the challenge or my best friend marching next to me, but from the voice deep inside me going quiet. At that moment, I was able to accept everything as it was, and in that acceptance I found a peace deeper than any I'd ever experienced. I had no doubts or worries. I took another step, and felt no pain.

25

For nearly two hours, I ambled along behind T, stepping carefully. Every few minutes, he would stop and look over his shoulder. "Still holding up back there?"

"Still breathing," I'd reply. "And still walking."

"Fair enough." And he would continue marching up the ever-steepening path.

Eventually, he paused ahead, waiting in silence. I managed to make up the twenty yards or so between us fairly quickly. Finding myself on relatively flat ground, I took the opportunity to glance around. "We resting for a bit, or what?"

"Nah." T shook his head.

"Well, then? I'm good. Let's keeping going."

"My brother," T said. "You know what's up ahead, next, don't you?"

"How am I supposed to know that? This is farthest that I've ever been."

"I saw it on the map, before we left. I recognize this spot. From that." He pointed ahead to where the trail took a sharp turn to the left and disappeared into the forest.

"Yeah, so what's up?" I strained my eyes to see just what was significant about the path taking another turn.

"About five hundred feet ahead, things are going to get... different."

"Okay." I nodded. "I'm not worried about it, let's just do it."

T looked at me. I could see the worry in his eyes. "How's that ankle holding up?"

"It's wonderful. Never felt better." I took several steps forward to prove my point, then took another long drag off of my cigarette. I exhaled slowly, still glancing at the path ahead, attempting to ascertain just what it was that had brought our journey to such a sudden halt.

He shook his head.

"You're getting into your own head," I said. "Whatever the hell's coming up, I can beat it. We can beat it."

"This, my brother, this is going to be something that I can't do much to help you with. Coming up, man, this is gonna be the worst part of it all. Especially since you've only got a leg and a half right now."

I shrugged. "Can't get that much steeper."

"Not steeper." He shook his head. "I've heard about what's coming up. It's called 'The Chute.' People have told me it's as rough as climbing in The Rockies. It's more than a quarter mile, almost straight up, where the path is nothing but a bunch of rocks. This is when it goes from hiking to mountain climbing, my friend."

"Well, I came up here to challenge this mountain, and that's what I intend to do. Besides," I said. "Some steep rocks can't be any scarier than a bear, right?"

"There's more after that," T said. "Some of these rocks are so tall and sheer you can't get up them at all. So, there are these ladders that have been bolted on to the rock faces. But they're pretty much straight vertical, all the way. Between those and The Chute, it's one of the toughest routes in the Appalachians, and that's with two functional legs."

"T," I said. "Listen to me, brother. I have no intention of letting this mountain beat us again. I don't care if both my legs are broken. I'll drag myself up the side of this damned cliff with just my arms. The only way I don't see that peak is if I die trying to get there."

"Hey, it's just a climb, I mean-"

"No!" I shouted. "It's not just a f...ing climb! This is more than that, and you know it. This is...this is everything! This is it! This is-"

"Brother." T's voice was calm. Almost serene.

I felt the emotion rising up inside me, but I did my best to keep my voice low. "No." I shook my head. "No."

"Brother," he repeated.

"We can't fail again. I can't fail again. I have to do this."

"And if you don't make it?"

"I'll make it," I said. "I have to make it. Things always have a way of working themselves out, right?"

"You can't manipulate that to mean, 'you always get what you want,' you know. We both know things never turn out how we expect." He paused. "Even if they are right in the end, one way or another."

"I can make it."

"Brother, I'm just saying, this is about to be rough, and if something goes wrong stuck between the ladders, or halfway up the chute, then-"

"Then I deal with it then." I was resolute. "I can do it. Trust me."

"I've always trusted you, my brother." A shadow fell across T's face and his gaze turned downwards. "But do you trust you? Think hard, here. There's some things you can't go back from. There are a lot of decisions you don't get to try to make a second time."

131

"You think I don't know that?"

"We both know that."

"Yeah," I said. "So trust me. I can do this."

"Okay," he said. A pause. "Okay. That's enough for me."

We both sat in silence for several minutes. I gazed upwards, trying to discern the path ahead through the trees. I couldn't see anything at all. Everything ahead of us was a complete mystery.

"You good?" T asked.

"Yeah," I said. "I got this. We got this. I'm ready whenever you are."

T smiled at me. It was a strangely peaceful smile, serene in its simplicity. "Okay." He turned and continued up the mountainside.

I followed behind. The rest–as brief as it was–left me feeling rejuvenated. I couldn't tell if the pain in my ankle was fading away or becoming easier to ignore, but it was bothering me less all the same. I took one step at a time, focusing on my breathing, and all discomfort fell to the wayside. I was on the right path–we were on the right path–and that was enough.

The sun beating down on our backs was warm and pleasant. The sweat and the pain all added to the enormity of the task we were well on our way to accomplishing. We were absorbing the energy of the world through our skin, taking in all of the strength of the universe and pushing forward. Our goal was within reach.

"T," I said.

"Yeah, brother?"

"I feel good, man."

"Yeah?"

"Yeah," I answered. "I know I can do this."

He laughed. "I've always known you could do this. You don't have to convince me."

I paused. "You seemed pretty worried a few minutes ago."

"No," he said. "I was sure. I just wanted to make sure that you were sure. This whole journey, everything... It's not our physical ability. It's our mindset. It's knowing we can do it. It's you knowing you can do it. If you're sure, that's enough for me."

"I'm sure," I said. "There's not a doubt in my mind. A little scratch and a twisted ankle isn't going to stop me. There're always obstacles, right?"

"Of course there are," T said. "It's not what happens to you, my brother. It's how you respond to it. I believe in you." He stopped for a moment, took a deep breath, and turned his head to look at the forest around us. We were silent, for a moment, breathing the mountain air in deeply. We listened to the birds chirping and the wind rustling through the leaves. "I've always believed in you, my brother. I know you won't let me down now."

The Ranch   26

M stared at me from across the desk. "So, you've only got a few days left."

"Yeah," I said. "I leave Saturday afternoon."

"And you've made arrangements?"

"I have. Gonna go out to my dad's house, maybe find time to watch a little football tomorrow. After that, just gotta buy some new gear and it's off to North Carolina. Grandfather's waiting for me."

She smiled at me. "So, that's really what you're going to do, then?"

"It is," I answered. "I mean, there's a lot to do after. But I just feel like this is something I have to do. A lot of things that happened... you know, I can't go back on most of them. I know, most of the time we don't get second chances. But this time, with the mountain, I can give myself a second chance. I can do it right this time. It's one thing I can make right."

"That's wonderful," Margot said. "But..." she paused. "Just remember that it's not everything. It's important to you, I know that. I think it's a wonderful step towards putting all of this behind you. But there has to be something after. You know that, don't you?"

"Of course." I leaned back and stared at the ceiling. "I've got a whole list of things to do. I can stay with my family a while. I've applied to a bunch of non-profits. Ya' know, like we talked about—get a job where I feel like what I do matters. All that good stuff. It all just seems... I dunno." I shook my head. "I know it's important, but none of it seems important. Does that make sense?"

"I think you could word it better," she answered. "But yes, I understand what you mean. But this trip you're planning, it seems important?"

"It does," I said. "It seems like the most important thing in the world. I know everything else is still there after... but if I do this, I can really accomplish something. And if I can accomplish that, why can't I accomplish everything else that I need to? I think it's the only way to start putting this behind me."

"Okay. I understand that. And we've gone over everything else—about what to do after and not letting this make or break you. I think you've heard about everything I have to say on the subject. So I'm not going to lecture you."

"Do you think it's the right thing to do?" I asked.

"For you," she said. "Yes, I do. It's important to you. And getting through everything, it's going to be a long, tough road. I think you're prepared for it. I think you understand the gravity of the situation and how hard it's going to be. I like that you're still afraid, because if you weren't afraid you'd be a fool. The only thing left you're lacking is complete confidence in yourself. You're still down on yourself, you still question every decision you've made. So, yes, I think this can be a great thing for you."

I smiled at her. "You know, Margot, I really do appreciate you. I know you've taken extra time to help me. I want you to know how much all of it means to me."

"I'm more than happy to help you," she said. "Because you want to be helped. And more importantly, you're willing to help yourself."

I nodded. There were a few moments of silence. "I really do think this climb is going to be the start of something. Even as much of everything as I've told you, I don't think I can really express how much it means. It's my white whale. I have to go back and defeat it."

"I know what you have to do. But," she cautioned. "Don't let the white whale take you down with it, Ahab."

27

The path lived up to its reputation. Within minutes, we were scrambling up a swath of rocks on our hands and knees. Even as I left a trail of dribbling blood along my route, the pain in my ankle was but a ghost of past failures. It no longer existed. The boulders became larger and taller, some wide enough to completely block the path. Those we climbed over, as the path narrowed to run between two large outcroppings of rock. It was as if some great ancient spirit of nature had forced itself through the mountain, scattering the remnants of a great wall of stone as it strolled merrily through the side of the mountain itself. We walked in its footprints, scrambling along the pebbles it had left in its wake that to us were giant boulders. The going was slow.

"Brother, brother, brother!" Shouted T, perched atop a shelf of stone twenty yards in front of me. "This is real mountain climbing, don't you think?"

"As real as the wind and the rain and that bear that nearly had you for lunch," I answered.

"Me?" T laughed. "That furry bastard wasn't going to have me for lunch. Pretty sure he thought you looked like a nice prime rib, though."

"Prime rib?" I shouted back. "You're giving me too much credit. I'm maybe on eye of round, at best."

T's laughter was booming. It bounced against the narrow rock walls and echoed into the valleys below. It filled the cool, thin air of the mountain and vibrated in every blade of grass that attempted to reach skyward between the field of boulders. "Let's call it a sirloin and leave it at that." Standing halfway up The Chute, he glanced upward, and then back down at me. "Either way, he had you pegged as dinner."

"It was really closer to lunch time."

"Brother, you don't know the bear's schedule. He hibernates and all. He was ready for an early meal."

"Can't say I was sorry to deprive him of it."

T smiled and shook his head. "Come on, let's keep it going, before you decide that little scrape is too much for you and turn around and fall back off a mountain."

"You can't fall off a mountain, T! Don't you know that?"

"Well, then, Kerouac, pick it up and get climbing, since there's nothing to be afraid of."

"It's Smith." I laughed at my own joke and scrambled up another five or ten feet, leaning forward with my hands against the rocks, pulling myself up as best I could and pushing with one leg while I tried to strain the other as little as possible. The sun, no longer obscured by trees as we grew ever closer to the peak, was slowly beginning to lower itself to the horizon. It was still bright and hot, blaring down upon my back. I stopped and took a long drink of water.

"No time for rest now, brother!" T was still scrambling up the ever steepening Chute, effortlessly, as if he was able to float just above the rocks.

"I'm gonna smoke," I said. "Give me a minute."

"No time. No time, no time! Let's get through this and then you can smoke and we can eat and we'll get camp all set up so we can be ready to make our final push at dawn."

"I'm going to smoke." Endless, shining optimism aside, the rush of my self discovery was beginning to fade, and the pain in my leg was beginning to increase. My ankle throbbed. I was afraid to lift my pant leg and witness exactly what shade of dark purple I was sure it had become.

"Do what you need to do." Calm as always, T climbed another few feet up the bed of rocks and found a particularly long and flat stone to sit on. He tossed his pack to the side and took a deep breath. "It smells like freedom up here."

"Yeah?" I said. I lit a cigarette.

"Yeah, brother! We're getting so close. Another few hundred yards of this, a few ladders, and then we're within spitting distance of relaxing for the rest of the day."

"Okay," I said. "Two minutes."

"Sure, sure."

I closed my eyes and smoked my cigarette. In the fresh mountain air, it didn't taste nearly as good as I had expected it would. Half-finished, I tossed it to the side and took a few careful steps up the path. "Hell, or now."

"That's the spirit!" He leapt up from his perch atop the rock and bounded up the path with several long strides. "As long as you don't defeat yourself, the mountain can't defeat you!"

"Some men aren't made for defeat!" I answered.

"Keep climbing, Hemingway." T laughed. He didn't look back, instead bounding up The Chute with renewed focus. The way he climbed looked effortless, dancing up the face of the cliff, hopping without care from rock to rock.

I followed after, as best I could, crawling on my hands and knees up the scattering of rocks. It wasn't long before the ladders were visible ahead. The first of them, carved out of wooden planks, ran vertically straight up the side of a massive boulder. At the base of it, I stopped and craned my neck upwards. Ahead of me, T was already scrambling up the ladder, his long arms stretching upwards to pull his body along the rock face. I took a deep breath, and launched myself forward, grabbing firmly onto the hand holds.

I reached with one arm, and then a second passed that, pushing my feet firmly against the horizontal beams as I struggled to pull myself upward. The first push off of my injured leg sent pain radiating through my body. It stretched into my spine, and I felt my grip loosening. Grinding my jaw, I ignored the sensation and clenched tighter. Seconds turned into minutes that could've been hours as I climbed higher, one ginger step at a time. When the top of my head finally rose above the top of the boulder, I was overcome with a sense of joy as the wind blew through my hair. I dragged myself onto the top of the boulder, only to find my newfound confidence disappear when I looked forward to see the trail in front of me. This was only the first of several ladders, each steeper than the last, criss-crossing a series of boulders standing between me and the rock shelf at the top of the trail.

T already stood at the top. He beckoned to me. As always, the only thing I could see was the massive grin stretched across his face. He peered down, smiling and waving his arms. "Just follow me, brother. You can do this."

My only response was a grunt as I dragged myself to my feet and set forward to climb the next ladder. I don't know how long the process took, but when I was finally lying at the top of The Chute I felt that I'd aged ten years. Every muscle in my body burned, screaming into the fading light that another step was impossible. My breath was short and ragged. I crawled forward on my hands and knees, my pack pressing down against my back. The sun above, brilliant and bright, no longer laughed at me. I felt its warm smile as I struggled to my feet.

T stood in front of me, glowing in the glory of the afternoon sunlight. He floated above the rock face, shimmering in the ecstasy of success. His arms were spread outwards in the shape of a cross as the wind whipped through his hair. "You've followed me to glory, my brother."

All I could do was laugh. It rose from deep inside my stomach, exploding in short bursts as I struggled to catch my breath. "What are you, Mountain Jesus?"

"I'm leading you to the peak, my brother."

"Wouldn't that make you more like Mountain Moses?"

"You're the one giving out names here, bro."

I shook my head. "We'll stick with T, then."

"Whatever you say." He shrugged. "I'm just here so we can get to the peak, right?"

"You're here—we're here—because we're friends." I paused a moment. "And because nothing can beat us. Not the d… water. Not the d… Chute. Not this messed up ankle or any d… bear. This mountain is ours."

"Then keep walking. It's not over."

So I did. I slung my pack onto my shoulders and ambled forward, one step at a time. The sun fell beneath the peaks as we hobbled slowly onward. Darkness came upon us as we set up camp, eating in silence and staring into the fire. Soon, sleep overtook us, as the same thought ran incessantly through my head. "Tomorrow, we'll conquer the peak, and life will begin anew."

 **28**

Autumn came to South Florida, and with it came hurricane season. I sat on the back porch, my eyes half open, with a cigarette dangling between my lips, as rain poured from the night sky. The wind was furious, sending rain drops and tree branches alike flying through the air to slam against the side of the building next door. Water pooled upon the concrete below, the ground already so saturated that it could hold no more. I paid none of it any heed.

My head leaned forward, involuntarily, as my eyes drooped shut. Just as my eyes fully closed, I jerked out of my chair with a start, swatting at my shorts. "What the heck?" A new, perfectly round burn hole was sitting just above my knee. My cigarette hissed as it hit the damp floor below, its embers extinguished. I examined the burn on my leg and, concluding that it was mostly superficial—nothing worth worrying about—I leaned back into my chair and lit another cigarette.

"You all right, bro?" T peeked his head through the open patio door. "You out here yelling at the hurricane again or what?"

"Nah," I mumbled, my eyes already closing again as I pulled on my new cigarette. "Just burned myself a little. Nothing really." I rolled my head to the side. "Nothing really, just a little... just a little burn, yeah."

T shook his head. "You're gonna set yourself on fire one day."

"Probably." I shrugged without opening my eyes. "Hey, 'least I'm out here and not in the bed this time."

"You and that smoking in bed junk. You're gonna nod out one day and burn this whole place to the ground."

"Probably." My cigarette, half-finished, slipped out of my mouth, and landed with a sizzle on the ground. "Lost 'nother one." I let loose some imitation of a laugh. It was a quick, single syllable grunt.

T sat down in the chair next to me, staring through the screen at the storm raging around us. "This is just the start of it, buddy. News said this thing's a category three. This is a real storm."

"Yeah, sure is," I slurred. I lit the wrong end of a cigarette and tossed it to the ground. "Dammit." I lit another one, with some difficulty.

"Can't believe you got Guy to drive out here in this," T said.

"Freaking, freaking d... " I fumbled at my pockets. "Time. Time is... What time is it?"

"I dunno, man. Probably like nineish."

"No." It was the clearest word I'd spoken in hours. "What time is it? Is it nine-thirty yet?"

T glanced at his phone. "Nine thirty-three."

"Shit." I stood up, still digging in my pockets, until my hand finally grasped my phone and pulled it out. The screen was cracked in several places, and the home button had long since fallen off. I dialed frantically.

"Bad news, man." The voice on the other end was low and muffled.

"Nah," I said. "Nah, don't tell me that. What's going on? I already got the cash out. Got it all here."

"What's going on? A hurricane. That's all!"

"So you didn't even leave or what?"

"I left," the voice answered. "I'm on Cypress Creek, past Powerline. But these little streets to get to you, they're all half flooded. I tried like three. It's not happenin'."

"I'll come to you," I offered. "Where exactly are you?"

"In front of that little airport entrance," he said. "Ya' not gonna make it, though. Not in that little car of yours. If I can't get through this flood, there's no way you can."

I stopped for a moment to consider the situation. "How long can you wait?"

"It's only gonna get worse if I wait. We'll just do it another time."

"No," I said. "No. No no no! I need to get it tonight. Tonight. I'm not gonna be sick during a damn hurricane. How long can you wait?"

"I told you, there's nothing to wait for, I..."

"I'm gonna walk. The sidewalks are higher up, for most of it. I think I know a way through."

"You're crazy."

"How long can you wait?"

He sighed. "How long do you need?"

I was already walking inside and grabbing my boots. "Fifteen minutes, tops. I'm leaving right now."

"You're crazy. Completely crazy."

"Fifteen minutes. I'll be there, at that little bus stop."

"Fifteen minutes." A moment of silence. "Don't die on me. I really don't feel like dealing with that." He hung up.

"You know," T said, standing in the frame of the open patio door. "You are crazy. You know that, right?"

"Guy said the same thing."

"See," T replied. "Even he's got more sense than you do."

I laughed, now fully awake, practically salivating at the thought of how I would spend the remainder of the evening. "It'll be a nice evening walk. A stroll in the park!"

"Wouldn't do it myself, but I'm damn glad you're going." T laughed. "Hurricane party, right?"

I was already walking out the front door. "It'll be a helluva party," I called back as the door slammed behind me.

As soon as I reached the bottom of the stairwell, the wind slammed against my body, nearly slamming me into the wall to my left. I staggered forward, turning left and keeping close to the side of the building as I made my way towards the road. The rain was beating against my back.

The power was still functional. I used the glow of the streetlights, enveloped in a haze of pouring rain, to guide myself toward the road. I stomped through puddles deep enough to soak into the tops of my shoes, pushing through a line of bushes to reach the sidewalk running along the side of the main road. The wind roared loudly, sending the rain drops crashing against my cheeks. They stung like bullets.

I patted my pocket to check for my phone, pushing it deeper inside to keep it safe from the water. Not a single car passed by. I took off at a light jog, shielding my eyes to find the stop sign that I knew was only a few hundred yards ahead. With every step I took water splashed up from the ankle deep puddles along the ground, soaking my jeans. The rain did the same to my shirt, and I was sopping wet by the time I reached the intersection only a minute later.

The wind whipped through the trees, pushing the branches as far as they could stretch. The storm was making landfall, and I could see that the road ahead was littered with a crumbling of fallen trees. I dashed across the road, paying no attention to the increasing depth of the water rising around my ankles. I slogged through the mess of water and mud and made a right down a side street. It was flooding worse than the main road.

My progress slowed as each step became a struggle. The water rushing past my calves threatened to sweep me off my feet. I could feel my phone vibrating in my pocket, though I couldn't hear it ringing over the raging fury of the wind and rain crashing down upon the darkened road. The streetlights flickered, briefly, and for a few moments the world around me was plunged into nearly complete darkness.

The lights flashed back to life, and I continued my laborious hike. I fought against the water, against the wind, and against the sinking feeling in the pit of my stomach as I felt my phone going off once again. *He better not be trying to leave.* The strength of my desperation forced me onwards.

In the distance, I could just barely make out the glare of headlights shining through the tempest. Against my better judgement, I pulled my phone from my pocket. I knew who both missed calls were from. I dialed back, ducking against a hedge to shield myself as much as possible. Water poured down from the sky.

"I see you!" I shouted, fearful he wouldn't hear me above the din of the open sky pouring its contents upon me.

"Don't see you. This is crazy." He was barely audible.

I fumbled with my phone and found the flashlight button. I flashed it several times, aimed at the direction of the headlights. "You see me?"

I received no answer.

I tried to flash the light again. Nothing. Looking down, I saw that my phone, overcome by a deluge of water, had shut off.

I raced forward. There was no rain, no water pooling on the sidewalk. There was only the glow of the headlights ahead of me, flashing faintly beneath the curtain of nature's fury.

As I drew closer, I saw the lights shift. They backed up and turned sideways. "No!" I screamed, my voice drowned out by the gusting wind. I felt tears streaming down my face as I willed my legs to move faster. "No, please no." My voice was merely a whimper now.

An eternal thirty seconds later I was standing along the side of the next main road, flailing my hands wildly as the headlights faded. I ran forward, splashing into the street as he turned around and began to drive back past me. At the last second, passing only a foot or two in front of my face, the vehicle skidded to a halt. Muddy water splashed into the air, coating my already soaked face and body.

The window rolled down just a crack. "You're crazy," he repeated.

I put my hands against the crack in the window, forcing several sopping wet bills through the small opening. "It's a hundred," I shouted.

Without a word, he pushed a ball of plastic wrap back out the window, into my outstretched hand. He was gone again in seconds. I stood there, hurricane rain pounding against my cheeks and listening to the wind howl, with a smile stretched across my face.

The feeling of elation lasted only a moment as a surge of water once again nearly swept me off my feet. I pushed the ball of plastic deep inside my pocket, forcing it beneath my broken phone. Come hell or high water, I would drown in a puddle before the package would get lost.

I turned around to begin my journey back home. For a brief moment, I saw the glint of the bus stop in my eye. Instantly, my mind was overtaken by a force I had no hope to control. I turned off of the sidewalk and forced my way, against the brutal winds, to the bus stop, where its three walls offered some small respite against the storm. In that moment, the insanity of my thinking was invisible to me.

I crouched down in a corner of the covering, as far from the rain as possible, and pulled a small pouch from my pocket. It had everything I needed. I pulled open the ball of plastic I'd just purchased, picking out a single small baggie, and dumping the rest into the pouch. It only took a moment of indecision to ignore my impulses towards logic. I picked the puddle that I decided was the cleanest, and leaned down to draw up fifty or sixty units. "Gotta heat it," I mumbled to myself, in what I imagined was a moment of clarity. "Don't need to catch a damn fever shot off this hurricane water."

I managed, somehow, to keep my lighter going for ten or fifteen seconds, and it was less than a minute later that I was threading my belt back through the loops in my jeans. "How do you like that, you stinking hurricane? You're from hell!" I shouted at the sky, taking a few steps forward and forgoing the meager protection offered by the bus stop. "You got nothin' on me!"

I grinned and stepped back out onto the sidewalk. I strolled through the storm like I was meandering along the beach on a sunny summer afternoon. Had I been capable of whistling, I would've, but instead I hummed a tune to myself as I moved without care through the puddles and raging water. I would make it home, I was sure, though I didn't quite care either way. Engulfed in my own warm, buzzing bubble, I watched the hurricane through a window at the back of my own eyes, letting my body take the beating while I relaxed by the fire in the cocoon inside my head. Inside there, it was warm and dry and nothing else mattered except dozing off on a beautiful summer evening.

29

I awoke and crawled out of the tent just as the sun was rising over the mountain peaks. The throbbing pain in my ankle did little to dampen the sense of joy I felt watching the morning materialize at the top of the world. In the distance, Attic Window loomed high, seeming almost within arm's reach. T was nowhere to be seen, but I paid that fact no heed. He always came back at the right time.

I boiled a cup of coffee over the still hot embers of last night's fire and took a moment to relax and soak in the morning. The shining sun mirrored the optimism rising within my heart. Years of pain and guilt amounted to nothing but mist in the morning air as I slowly sipped my drink. I lit a cigarette and hobbled over to the spot where my pack was leaning against a tree. I rustled through it, reaching towards the bottom, where my treasures resided.

I pulled the scotch out first, tracing my fingers along the label. Deep inside my stomach, I could already feel the warmth it would bring with the first sip. I remembered something I'd read once, a quote that Kerouac had attributed to some ancient Zen Master by way of the inimitable Gary Snyder: "The first sip of tea is joy, the second is gladness, the third is serenity, the fourth is madness, the fifth is ecstasy." I'd never possessed quite such a passion for tea, but the thought of the decades old Scottish sliding along my palette brought similar feelings. The ecstasy would come, I was sure, in far fewer than five sips, especially if I intended to be in any shape to march back down the mountainside after.

I flicked my tongue along my lips, imagining the taste of victory that was so close. I tasted every oaky note that would dance along my pallet when I finally poured the golden liquid down my throat at the top of the peak. I imagined it would be, tea or not, the truest taste of ecstasy that I would ever experience.

In that moment, I remembered my grandfather, sipping slowly on a glass of Wild Turkey as he bounced me on his knee nearly three decades earlier. I thought of long summer afternoons in my youth, T and I tromping through the Tennessee woods. I could see the first tree house we built, crooked and barely hanging on to the branches, as we climbed onto the roof and surveyed the yard below. Our victory then mirrored the victory that was soon to come, standing on top of the world and looking down upon the endless kingdom that we could call our own.

I put the scotch away, tucking it carefully into the bottom of my pack between several folded shirts. From the farthest depths of the pack I pulled a small wooden box, the same box that I'd so carefully examined at the start of my journey. It looked the same, on the outside, made of a smooth dark wood, pristinely polished. It was closed tightly, and would remain that way. I flipped it over, examining the bottom, where a few small, nearly invisible letters had been carved. They were ornate without the trappings of décor, just three simple letters cut carefully into the wood in a thin, flowing script.

I had no idea who had taken the time to carve the letters. In a way, I liked to imagine that unknown soul had spent months, crouched carefully in an old workshop that smelled of cedar and pine, spending weeks carefully tracing each letter over and over in perfect form. They would've done it with the utmost respect, treating the small box as a sacred relic of some ancient god, assiduously performing each tiny stroke so as to appease the will of the world that demanded nothing but perfection here.

I weighed the box in my hands, moving it up and down, examining each grain of the wood. I felt its weight carefully. It was strange how something so valuable, containing such infinitely wise memory, could be so light. I made no effort to open it. It could not be opened, not yet. I tucked the box close, holding it against my heart, and exhaled deeply. My breath offered no life to the treasure, but I gave it nonetheless; I offered my breath willing and freely, but nothing came of it. The box lay still, clasped tightly in my hands, its smooth wooden surface pressed against my chest.

After another moment of reflection, I tucked the box back away into my pack, wrapping it with the same loving care that I had offered the glass bottle of scotch. I piled my remaining clothes back on top of the items. The air, in that infinite second, was still and silent. The heat of the sun faded away.

Despite the serenity of my surroundings, I felt my heart racing as old memories stirred. I knelt down and closed my eyes. In my mind, I floated away from the mountain, into the past. I swam through time to my last night in Florida, when the whole world had collapsed into a hellish black hole, and I had emerged believing that salvation would lay forever beyond my reach.

 # 30

I stood in the haze of an unknown Florida night, tears soaking my face in a way that the unending rain never could. Behind me, the last remnants of a sterile white light flashed behind the spectar of impregnable glass doors. They were doors that I could never reenter. While the world faded at my back, before me lay only darkness. I had no will left to turn around, and instead, step by miserable step, marched forth into that all encompassing darkness.

I walked for endless steps as I cried endless tears. I trudged deeper into the void, the only direction I could bear to go. I begged for it to envelop me, to take me into its cold grasp and let me rest. I demanded it take me as an offering, wrap its arms around me and give back to the world that light that was ever further behind me. I screamed for it, my voice drowned out in an endless sea of unnamed voices that all cried out the same.

I wanted to yell out for T, my ever faithful friend, to reach out his hand and drag me from this endless place where light and love had no meaning. I knew he couldn't reach me any longer. Here, there was nothing to do but dive deeper, to push on into the suffocating night on some vain hope that soon it would steal my breath, too. What was real and unreal blurred together. My thoughts were not my own, and every deed I'd ever done had only been in service to this inevitable end of all that was hopeful and good in the world.

I don't know how long I walked before I was lying upon a sidewalk, three inches deep in a puddle of fetid water. I imagined the torrent that rushed through the gutters was a product only of my own tears. I lay there for days, maybe weeks. Neither the tears nor the rain would cease, yet the water never rose above my mouth. I was always lying there, mere inches from drowning, with each breath somehow more painful than the last. The darkness didn't take me, though I would've begged it to, had my voice not been so hoarse from screaming.

I kept waiting for a voice to break through the night and tell me it was all only a nightmare, or even a prank. It would be a horrible, sadistic prank, but one that I would gladly embrace if I could only know that the sun would rise again the next day. I would bargain with the world. I would sell my soul to step back a day and steer the ship away from the storm, but the chance wouldn't come.

The darkness of this phantom night would always be a part of me. But not in the way I thought then. Though nightmares may leave their mark even when the day breaks, even the worst of dreams can't go on forever. Though I didn't believe it, then, the light would come eventually, on a damp gray dawn, one ray at a time, at the top of a mountain that had long ago faded away into memory.

31

"**B**rother! Hey, brother, you all right?"

My eyes shot open, wide with surprise. I was leaning against a tree, facing the morning sun, clutching my pack tightly in my arms. I wasn't sure if I'd fallen asleep or just drifted away upon the tide of memory. Back into the warmth and light of the mountainside, I wasn't sure I cared either way where I had come from.

"What's happening?" T stood next to me, his back to the sun, obscuring his features in a blanket of shadow.

"Nothing." I shook my head. "Nothing, really. Just staring down some demons, I suppose."

"Helluva way to spend such a beautiful morning. What're you doing staring at demons when you could be climbing a mountain?" When I didn't answer right away, he crouched down next to me. "They didn't stare back, did they?"

"They always do," I said. "Even when I'm not looking at them. What is it, again? 'If thou gaze long into an abyss, the abyss will also gaze into thee.' I mean-"

"Today's not the morning for this, my brother. Tell ol' Fred to leave my friend alone and get off our mountain. We have a job to do today."

"Yeah, I know. I just... Hell, mindful as I can be, sometimes it all comes back to me. The weight of everything is a lot to bear."

"Good thing you've been getting a good work out in, then, huh? Gettin' stronger so you can carry that weight, bro."

I shook my head. "Ah, T, ya' know what I mean."

"Of course I do," he said. "I always know what you mean. That doesn't mean I agree with it though."

"It's not a matter of agreeing, it's just…"

"Of course it is," he interrupted. "I swear, it's like we're always having a variation of the same conversation. The weight of the world is only heavy if you let it be. The demons can only see you when you stare at them. Turn your head and look up at the sun! There's nothing that matters behind you. The light is up ahead, my friend."

"Sure," I said, glancing upwards. "But I'm getting old and I'm down to one good leg. I'm not in much shape to be running away from anything."

T laughed, the booming rumble echoing against the silent peaks of the mountaintops. "Then keep on moving, before they get you. There's no time for sadness today, my friend."

"I'm sure I can find a little time."

"Nah, brother," he said. "Come on, get up. Get up, get up. Let's get our shit packed and get a move on. This is the home stretch. It's time we move."

"Gimme a minute." I reached into my pocket and found a cigarette.

"Whatever you say." He shrugged. "Time doesn't mean anything to me, ya' know. You're the one letting the past chase you up the side of a damn mountain. I'm just along for the ride."

"Nah, buddy. This isn't you tagging along on my journey. This is you and me. Just like it's always been." I smiled and lifted my head. "I'm ready. I've been ready."

"Whatever." He bounded a few steps forward, still appearing as a shadow against the rising sun. His featureless form sailed gracefully beneath the sky, the grass beneath his feet remaining untouched as he moved.

I stood up. It didn't take more than fifteen minutes to pack up camp. When we finished, I lingered by the fire, staring off into the distance. I let thoughts float through my mind, but paid each one no heed. I simply watched as they passed by, passing no judgment. The endless images of past and present strolled through the landscape of my mind, chattering with unheard voices, but they were simply thoughts, nothing more. I am not my thoughts. For a moment, I simply was, standing there on the precipice of redemption.

Without another word, T began to walk, leading the way along the path. I followed after. We didn't speak, for a while, as I chased his formless shadow. Slowed by my ankle, I would lose sight of him from time to time, only to find him standing just beyond each curve in the path. No matter which direction we were traveling, winding along the last legs of the trail, he was always facing the sun when I found him again. I took refuge in his shadow, shielding my face from the harshest of the burning rays shining down from the sky. Even when the brightness threatened to obscure my vision, in following his shadow I was able to find my way forward.

The Ranch   32

The morning of my last day was the warmest of the week. I stood outside, basking in the glow of the October sun, surrounded by the friends I'd made over the last month. Margot stood behind the group, alongside all the others who had been kind enough to wake me up and bring me coffee and do everything else they'd done for me since I'd arrived. She smiled at me, and I smiled back.

My friends congratulated me, offering words of encouragement. We hugged and shook hands. We laughed and cried. We promised that we'd all see each other again. Some of them, I would. Others would fade away, turning into vague memories as time passed. It felt almost like a high school graduation. Back then, when everyone promised to be friends forever and never lose touch. And then, just a few years later, you struggle to remember most of their names. I knew, on some level, that this would be the same. But, in that moment, none of it mattered. At that exact moment in time, we were all the closest of friends. At that exact moment in time, no other moment existed.

As the small crowd milled about, wondering who would be leaving next, Margot made her way over to me. "I told you it would come faster than you would believe."

I smiled at her. "You were right, Margot. Just like always."

"How're you feeling?"

"Good, actually. Really good. I mean, I'm sad to leave everyone. But I'm ready. I'm ready for the outside world. I'm ready to really be better. I'm ready for that damned mountain."

"You're going to do great," she assured me. "The mountain doesn't stand a chance.

"Thanks,Margot." I grinned. "I'm... ya' know, I'm not just gonna miss my new friends. Everyone here has been so great, even at the beginning when I was something less than pleasant to be around." I felt the tears forming in the corners of my eyes. "I'm really gonna miss you,Margot. I'm pretty sure you saved my life."

"Don't do that on your last day. All I did was listen and help you make sense of your own thoughts. You saved your own life." And then, her tone softened. "But, I'll miss you, too. It has been a pleasure having you here. I'm so proud of you."

"Thanks,Margot. I wish I could've learned all this years ago, and maybe it would've been different."

"You're living in the past, again," she cautioned. And then she laughed. "Come on, don't thank me and then forget everything we talked about ten minutes before you leave."

"I'll try to remember at least half," I joked, laughing alongside her. "I am sorry to go, though, in a way. I feel like, as long a month seemed, it's not a lot of time when you're learning things that're gonna change the rest of your life."

"Look," she said, and stepped a little closer. "I know, as I've told you, that the policy is that we don't take on anyone from here as an aftercare patient. It could be seen as a conflict of interest."

"I know, Margot, and I…"

"But." She handed me a small piece of folded paper. "I do run a free weekly group meeting. Because I'm not charging for it, I don't see any reason I can't invite you to attend. Keep my number, and let me know if you can ever make it. We'd be happy to have you."

I tucked the paper into my pocket. "Thanks,Margot." I felt tears coming to my eyes again. "I really do appreciate that. I'd love to come sometime."

"You're welcome to come any time," she answered. "And if you ever really need anything... you know, if you find yourself standing on that precipice and don't know what to do, you can call me. I would much rather answer my phone at three in the morning than to wake up and hear that they found you dead in a ditch somewhere."

"I will,Margot."

"I mean it." Her voice was taking on that stern tone again, the one she used when she wanted to make sure we all knew just how serious she was. "I know you don't like to ask for help. But there's no shame in it. If you need to, you call me. Promise me."

"Of course," I said. "I promise. I kept my last one, right?"

"You did," she said. "And you damn well better keep this one!" She laughed. "I know you'll be okay, but I'd like to hear from you just to confirm the fact.

I wasn't sure why, but I felt a sudden tinge of sadness. "M, do you really think I'll be okay? Like, really okay? I don't mean just getting by and not letting it all tear me down. I mean where I don't have to constantly remind myself all the time not to live in the past or future, or where I don't still wake up at night in cold sweats wondering if it's all crashing down around me."

"You will," she said. "It won't happen right away. You have to work at it. You have to try—and trust me, it'll be the hardest thing you've ever had to do in your life. But one day, you'll be where you want to be. It's never going to be perfect. Life is always going to be a bumpy ride. But the day's going to come when you're okay, even if it takes a little bit. But when it comes, you'll know it."

33

As the morning moved into afternoon, I ignored the subtle words of exhaustion whispering in my ear. I was long past paying attention to the complaints of my body. The peak was close now. I caught glimpses of it between the trees whenever I dared to lift my head from the path below.

The closer we got to Attic Window, the more I found my mind drifting back to everything that had led me here. I kept thinking back to Margot, and everything she'd told me when I was back West trying to get my head right. It had seemed impossible, in those days, that anything could end well. Back then, this journey had just been a half-baked fantasy to get me through the days. And yet, here I was, following the shadow of T, snaking up the last end of the path to reach the peak that had eluded me before.

I felt the fingertips of sadness tickling at the back of my mind, but pushed them away once again. "Is this the right way, M?" I asked, knowing an answer couldn't come. "Am I really starting over, or am I just hanging on to the same old shit?"

"You say something, buddy?" T's voice broke through my moment of doubt. He was standing thirty or forty yards ahead, framed in the glory of the afternoon sun.

"Just mumbling to myself," I said. "Talking to people who aren't here, as always."

"Well, it's a good thing we both know you're not crazy, huh? Because you sure are pushing the line." I could hear his booming laughter. "Worry less about all that, and more about finishing this damn climb. We're close, and I know you've gotta be exhausted."

"T." I felt those old familiar feelings creeping back up. I felt the past clawing at my back. "This whole thing, I'm wondering if it's really what we needed. I mean, hell, we're too damn old to be taking off and running from the world up the side of a mountain."

"First off," he answered. "You can get as old as you want, but I have no intention of letting that happen to me. Besides," he shook his head. "We both know this is what has to happen. Hell, it's not just you who needs this. This is the right thing. It's the right thing for me, too, you know. It's not running from anything. Now, do you want to make things right, or are you going to crawl back into that black hole of yours and let the world leave you behind?"

"Make things right?" I shook my head. "T, none of this is ever gonna be right. It's just making it all less wrong, and I'm getting too tired of playing not to lose."

"Then don't, my brother." I never saw him move, but he was suddenly back at my side. "Things never work out the way you want them to. Hell, we don't live in a d--- fairy tale. You've known that since you were in Middle School, you cynical bro, so why are you suddenly acting like this is all new to you?"

"No," I said. "Not this. It wasn't supposed to be like this. It was…"

"It wasn't supposed to be like anything!" T wasn't smiling. "Things are what they are. You're the one throwing all this stuff around about accepting what is and mindfulness and living in the moment, and when you're finally within reach of doing the only thing left that you want to do, you get scared and start making excuses? Brother, that's not you. That can't be you."

"I dunno," I said. "Maybe it is me. I mean, I'm standing right here, letting these words come out of my mouth, right? I'm living in the moment, that means this is me."

"You're goddamn frustrating." He shook his head. "A few seconds of doubt isn't living in the moment, it's letting the past take over this moment. You know this is what you wanna do, so do it! I don't see the issue."

"T, I-" I stopped talking. I took a deep breath and stared up at the sky above. This wasn't the time to argue, or the time to be the same person I'd been before. "You're right," I finally said. "This is what I wanna do. I'm just afraid that... Well, I've put every thing into this. I've told myself over and over that if I can just make it to that peak, everything is going to be better. It's not like that, though..."

"Listen, bro, I think-"

"Nah, T," I interrupted. "Hold up, hold up a second. What I'm saying is... well, you know when you're reading a book, or watching a movie, and it finally gets to that climax at the end. You get a happy ending. You get the girl. Or hell, even if it's not happy, you get some sense of closure. The story's over. I mean, sure, Kerouac comes off his mountain and thinks about ol' Japhy and the shack and just goes, 'Blah!' and that's that, a suitable end to the journey. There's no book that ends with the poor slob angry and alone drinking himself to death in a goddamn tiny house in Florida."

T didn't answer. He stood there, waiting.

"Hell, man, sometimes I don't know exactly what I want to say. But it makes sense, right? You think there's some big ending, some shiny moment when it's all solved, but it doesn't work like that. The story doesn't just end in smooth sailing. All I want to is reach that peak... and then what? What happens then? I climb back down the damn mountain and nothing has changed, and I'm still angry and alone, staying up late at night thinking about all the terrible choices I made and horrible things I've done."

"Brother," T said. "Slow down, slow down. That's just life. Of course it's not all wrapped up in a neat happy ending, but that doesn't mean it doesn't matter. Sure, when you climb back down from here, the world is gonna be the same old place. But try to tell me that you won't be different when you come back down. Maybe you won't be a new person, but you'll be better. What the hell else can you ask for than to be better than you were before? Isn't there always some old Hemingway quote about that you're always spouting off about?"

"Yeah." I paused, picturing the words in my mind. I spoke slowly, trying my best to remember them just right. "The quote... 'There is nothing noble in being superior to your fellow man; true nobility is being superior to your former self.' It's a good quote."

"Damn right it is!" T shouted. "And that," he pointed up towards the peak of the mountain. "My friend, that is a noble goal. You really think that, when you walk down this mountain, you're not going to be a better man than when you walked up here? You think you won't be better than you were back in Florida? Or even off at that crazy old whatsis-ranch you spent that time at?"

I didn't respond. Instead, I just stared into the distance.

"If you won't answer," he said. "I will. Of course you'll be better. You were better than you were the moment you stepped onto this trail. You'll be better at the peak. And hell, when you get down, you'll be better then, too. That's the thing, my brother, is that you're right about there being no happy endings. All there are is a series of events and people and feelings that, hopefully, when it finally is time to pass on, you're happy to look back on and know you did more good than bad. There are always things to make up for, but I promise you, if you turn around now you will regret it for the rest of your life. You won't get another chance at this. I don't get another chance at this. You know that."

I nodded. "Yeah, T, I know. It's just... hell, it's scary. Everything went into getting better. And now everything's been going into this. My whole world, it's getting to the top of this mountain. What the hell do I do after that?"

"I dunno," T said. "But you'll figure it out. And whatever you do, wherever you decide to go next, you'll keep getting better. It's awesome that there's no storybook ending, if you think about it, because what the hell would there be to do after that? We'd all have to kill ourselves right at our most triumphant moment, because it would all be downhill from there. If you ask me, that would be a helluva lot more depressing, if that were true."

"Well," I said. "I guess we better get walking, then. We have a mountain to climb, after all."

My Friend T   34

It's funny the reasons why I remembered my first date. I barely remembered what she looked like, and I'm not sure I recall her name. I know I was nervous, but I never did associate the whole ordeal with much feeling. I'm not sure if I liked her much, or if I was thrilled to just be on a date. I want to say I was fourteen or so, in Middle School for sure, but I don't know exactly. I wasn't old enough to drive, and I was, without a doubt, completely clueless. What I do remember, though, is that it was a double date.

I was an awkward kid. I was tall and skinny, back then, and I was just as experienced with dating as I was with flying a plane, or the finer points of quantum theory. Despite my inability to discern the intentions of the opposite sex in even the most basic of situations, I found myself on a double date, thanks to the machinations of T. Executing a particularly ballsy move in the food court of the local mall, he was able to set up, for the both of us, a plan to take a set of twins from the school on the other side of town to dinner, followed by a movie, on a Friday night in late April of our eighth grade year.

We were both thrilled, of course, to finally be entering the world of teen romance that a hundred movies had promised us would end in lifelong happiness, despite a few awkward situations that would certainly all but solve themselves in a half hour or less.

We met the girls at a restaurant—I think it was a Chili's or some sort of comparable chain restaurant built to give middle American families and poor teenagers the illusion of a fine dining experience. The commercials sold what the food couldn't, but I was thrilled to be there. I had two twentys tucked into my wallet, thanks to a generous donation by my father. Given our age and the sum of the life experience it brought, we didn't know any better than to immediately go inside and begin to gorge ourselves on complimentary chips and salsa.

The girls eventually arrived, stepping nervously among tables and craning their necks. They scanned the room for a familiar face, their eyes darting back and forth. After several agonizingly long moments, they spotted us slouched low in our seats at a table near the back, completely unaware of our surroundings. We were shoveling chips into our mouth, already deep into conversation about the last video game that had temporarily secured our complete devotion.

"Hi, T!" Squealed the first girl. "This is gonna be so fun!" When he didn't stand up, she slid into the booth, wrapping her arms around his neck and planting a kiss on his cheek. "This," she said, "is my sister Morgan. Isn't she cute?" She motioned to the identical girl standing next to her, hovering next to the side of the booth where I was sitting.

"Uh huh." T barely looked up from the menu, instead absorbed in pouring over the substantial selection of fajitas. "Oh," he said, suddenly lifting his head. "This is my cousin. He's awesome, man. Funnest guy I know."

I managed to mutter a muted, "Hi."

Morgan sat next to me. "Hi, it's nice to meet you!" I couldn't tell if the smile on her face was one of joy or pity. To my teenage brain, it seemed obvious that it must be the latter. "I've heard so much about you. T says you're so smart and so much fun."

Encouraged, I uttered the most eloquent of responses that I could think of. It was nearly Shakespearian. "Cool. You too."

We ordered food and made awkward small talk while T and his date spoke in whispers, smiling at each other. Between bites of nachos, I volunteered that I had been more than impressed with the recent Green Day concert I attended—the first concert in my young life.

"That's the first time you've been to a concert?" Morgan was incredulous. "I went to my first concert when I was twelve. I saw TLC. They were just awesome." She continued to ramble on about that experience for the next ten or fifteen minutes. Not knowing any better, I expressed my disinterest by staring out the window.

"You know," she said. "You're not a lot of fun. Do you even know how to talk or what?"

"I, uh... yeah," I stammered. "I talk a lot. Sometimes. Sometimes I don't." I could feel my the warmth flushing in my cheeks as both girls stared at me. "I guess I don't know what to talk about."

T's date stared at me for a second, and then turned to him. "Your friend is weird."

"So?" The tone of T's voice changed in an instant. "If everybody was the same, everything would be boring. He's cool as hell, and he's my best friend."

"Ugh," said Morgan. "I don't know why I let you two talk me into this. This is my first date, and I'm stuck with some skinny weirdo who listens to stupid punk music."

I lowered my head, but remained silent. I wasn't about to open my mouth and ruin the night for everyone. But T had other ideas.

"He's weird, huh?"

"Yeah," she answered. "Weird. I don't even known why I'm here right now."

"I told you," his date chimed in. "This was a stupid idea. You're cool, T, but that doesn't mean we want to hang out with your dumb friends."

"My dumb friends?" He shook his head. "God, you're such a witch."

The look of absolute shock and confusion on her face was priceless, but he left her no time to answer. "I was trying to go have a nice time with a girl who I thought seemed nice, and not even a half hour into it, you start making fun of my best friend because he's a little nervous on his first date? You don't know him. You don't know anything about him. If this is the garbage you and your sister want to pull, I'm glad you started early, because he's too good to deal with your bull."

"No, no," I said. "It's cool. I... I know, I just..."

"Nah," T said. "They think they can sit here and talk about you like you don't matter. Squash that." He looked pointedly at them. "You don't have any right to judge him. Hell, you barely know me any better, so I don't think you have any right to judge me, either. Because if you were under the impression that I'm the kind of guy who is gonna let anybody talk bad about my best friend—for no reason ==then I'm obviously not the person you think I am."

Neither of them responded. I stared straight forward, refusing to meet their eyes, but I could feel their gazes.

171

"Come on," T said. "Let's get out of here." He motioned towards the door before turning back towards the girls and setting a pile of cash on the table. "Enjoy your dinner. It's on us. Come on, let's go."

I followed him out of the restaurant, staring at the ground in front of my feet. I was overcome with shame and embarrassment. I lit a cigarette—a habit I had only newly acquired. For a moment, I smoked silently while watching the cars drive by. "I'm sorry, T."

"Sorry?" He scoffed. "You don't have a damn thing to be sorry about. If somebody wants to judge you before you've said ten words, then to heck with them. Hell, if they wanna judge you after you said ten thousand words, forget them, too."

"Look," I said. "I know I messed things up here. It's cool—really cool—that you brought me along and tried to help me out. But we all know what I am, T, I'm—"

"You're my best friend, that's what you are." He shook his head. "You're my brother. You always have been. We stick together. We always stick together."

"Yeah, but, T-"

"We. Stick. Together." He shook his head. "It's not a hard concept. You'd never turn your back on me, and I'll be darned if I'm not gonna stick by you just the same."

"You didn't have to bring me along, though. I could've just hung out with the guys in the neighborhood, and let you do your thing, and you'd be having a great time right now."

"Bullshit," he snorted. "She said she had a friend who wanted to go on a date with a cool guy, so I brought along the most awesome friend I know. If they can't recognize that, I wouldn't have been having fun. I would've been hanging out with people who don't get me."

172

I lit another cigarette. Even then, moderation wasn't one of my strong suits. "I'm only draggin' ya' down, T. I mean, she was right. I am weird."

"Bro, cut that out." He followed behind me as I wandered down the sidewalk behind the restaurant. "You don't get to decide what other people think of you. Drop all that self-hating crap and take a look at the people around you. Nobody has to stick around, but all your friends do, because you're worth being around. And you're not my best friend because you're some piece of dirt." He didn't wait for me to respond. "Come on, let's get the hell out of here. We'll go call our real friends and play some night football at Regional Park."

35

We'd only been climbing for another half hour or so before I stopped to take a rest. Despite the aching in my body, and the burning in my chest from the increasingly strenuous terrain, I decided that the best course of action was to stop, smoke a cigarette, and stare blankly ahead. As we had gained altitude, we'd climbed into the mists that had given the mountains their name. We were passing through a particularly dense pocket, and on a previously clear day I could suddenly barely see more than a few yards in front of me.

T disappeared, as he always did, floating off into the fog and the memories. I stayed at our camp, lost in my own thoughts. As I was drowning in visions of the past, a sudden breeze stirred across the mountain, pushing the fog aside. Suddenly, I could see ahead, and there, not more than twenty feet away, was a brown signpost. It was nondescript, standing only a few feet off the ground. I moved a feet closer and read the words. "Attic Window: 1000 yards."

"T!" I shouted, my voice suddenly jubilant.

"Yeah, brother?" He wasn't far ahead, resting against a rock just passed the signpost.

"Did you see the sign?"

"If you're about to start singing Ace of Base, I swear to God, I will hurl myself off the side of this mountain."

"Dammit." I shook my head. "You passed it, before the fog cleared."

"And it said?"

I ran forward, almost skipping, to catch up to him. "A thousand yards! We're a thousand yards from victory!"

"Well," he said. "Finally, you give me some good news. You ready to drop the sad stuff and hit that peak?"

"I'm ready to put every bit of sad shit that ever happened in my entire life behind me and hit that peak." I was already five steps ahead of him. We were suddenly filled with a boundless, joyous energy. The pain in my body faded away as I pushed my way up the final ascent. T floated behind me, steady as ever.

I could hear his voice at my back. "You got this, brother. You got this." It somehow sounded farther and fainter with each word he spoke, but I was consumed only with reaching the peak. The sky was suddenly clear, and the sun shone radiant above. It bathed me in its warm glow. I was full of life.

With each step I took, I could feel the pull of Grandfather. The mountain no longer drove me back, but dragged me forward. Grandfather's ancient fingers reached out to me. I grabbed his bony, gnarled fingers, and felt no shame in accepting his helping hand as salvation drew ever closer. The universe smiled down upon me, and I smiled back.

T hovered just a few feet behind me. I paid no heed to the ankle that screamed at me with every step. "If I fall down, you're gonna help me back up again, right?"

"Always, brother," came the voice from behind me. "I'm your friend. Gotta have your back, right?" I was sure he was grinning.

"Didn't mean it that literally." I couldn't help but laugh. I was light and free, taking the final steps towards conquering the world that had for so long weighed heavy upon my shoulders.

"I know what you mean," T said. "Always do. Always have. Almost there now, come on."

He was next to me, by then, floating up the side of the mountain. I glanced over at him and the most genuine feeling of happiness that I had felt in years stretched across my face in the form of a smile. I was ragged and dirty. My clothes were ripped and torn. Mud was streaked down my skin, mixing with bits of leaves and dried blood to form the kind of miserable visage that made me look like I'd just stepped off the set of a Vietnam War movie. His countenance was clear, his faced unstained. He looked like he hadn't aged in years, charging ever upwards towards the heavens. As I grunted and grimaced with effort, his face was serene. As I huffed and puffed, breathing so rapidly that I could barely take in air, he moved forward in silence.

The last hundred feet were a blur. Time slowed down. I remembered playing football in the yard. I remembered my first day of school. I remembered my first date, my first beer, and the first time I ever decided that I needed to scale the side of a challenging mountain. I also remembered the second time. I remembered everything, and saw it for what it was. Time left me behind, and the world stood still as I finally set foot upon Attic Window Peak.

 36

"I'm sick, T."

"Yeah," he said, "I know. But brother, it's a beautiful night. Come on, this place I heard about, they do this hand-rolled sushi that's supposed to be incredible, and then they've got this soup-"

"T!" I shouted. "I can't eat. I can barely drink whatever. A million dollars wouldn't get me out from under this blanket." I lay in a dark corner of my Florida apartment, wrapped in a pile of sweat—stained blankets. My back was pressed against the wall. My window was open.

"So go do what you gotta do and get right. Come on, man, we've been planning this for months. It's gonna be awesome. I already told you, I'm covering you on this."

"I'm kickin' it, man. Tired of living like this." I shivered and closed my eyes. "I was gonna grab one more, taper it down a bit, make it easier... No money, though. Gotta wait 'till tomorrow."

Anyone else would've stared at me in disgust, but his was a look of pity. He sighed. "I swear to God, I feel like I'm shaking hands with the devil." He reached into his pocket and dropped a single twenty down. It fluttered into my lap. "Go get yourself right, and let's enjoy the night."

"You're a good friend, T."

"I dunno," he said. "Sometimes I think I'm the worst friend in the world."

It wasn't five minutes later that we were speeding down 95. I was still in my vomit-stained, sweat-soaked clothes. I dialed my phone frantically while weaving in and out of traffic.

"Slow down, brother!" T was pushed all the way back in his seat. "You're gonna kill the both of us."

"I won't," I said, clinching the steering wheel so tightly that my knuckles were shaking. I rolled down the windows, hoping to soften the scent of two days spent rolling in the dark in a mass of damp blankets.

"Just slow it down a little, huh?"

I pressed the gas harder. Several silent minutes later, we were parked in an alley behind a laundromat in Hollywood. My hands were shaking as a I struggled to prepare everything. I stuck once, twice, three times, but saw no red. Finally, on the fourth try, a trickle of brightness leaked in, and I immediately jammed the plunger down as hard as I could.

The relief was nearly instant. I sat for a moment, drawing a series of deep breaths. "Thanks, T"

He shook his head. "Don't thank me for this. This isn't right."

"No, T," I mumbled, already lighting a cigarette. "It's right, it's so right. Just helping me get through the night, ya' know? Tomorrow, the kick'll be a little easier. And then a few days... it'll all be gone."

"Do you really believe that?"

"Yeah," I lied. "Of course I do. Why, you don't?"

"I believe in you," he said. "But some things are bigger than you. The strongest man in the world still can't lift a mountain."

"I could beat a mountain," I shot back.

He shook his head. "I'm sure you could, my friend. You could do a lot've things, if you weren't all caught up in this bullshit."

"Like you're perfect."

"Come on!" He said, anger seeping into his voice. "Not sayin' I am. We know what I need to fix. But brother, you're slipping further and further down the slope. I'm not here to judge you, but I'm getting afraid that one day it'll get to steep for you to climb back up."

"I'll be okay. Just like you'll be okay. This... this isn't how it'll be forever."

"I hope not," T answered. "This could be me just as much as you. It's all part of life... but that doesn't mean it doesn't take effort to change it all."

"I'm putting in the d--- effort!" I snarled. "I told you, I'm doing it this time. I'm so tired, T."

He just stared straight ahead. I could barely hear his voice when he responded. "And when you get paid tomorrow, you're not gonna be sitting back here again?"

"Nah," I said. "This one. This was the last one. Tomorrow's gonna be different. Soon, everything's gonna be different."

He sighed. "I believe in you. I always have, my brother."

I didn't answer as I pulled the car back onto the northbound highway. I didn't want to lie, but in the back of my mind, I knew I was lying. I knew that the same old fear would always catch up to me, and I'd always be doing the same old things. T, I knew, would get past all this. He had the strength I couldn't dream of. He had a peace within him that nothing in the world could touch.

"You okay there, brother?"

"Yeah, T." I stared out the window. "Just thinking about things. Finding some comfort in the fact that, no matter what I've become, I know that you're going to rise above all this bull one day."

"We both will," he said. "Maybe in our own different ways. But we'll do it. One day, my friend, we'll both be free."

37

I stood at the top of Attic Window peak and surveyed my kingdom below. As afternoon had come, the fog had all but faded away. The world was laid bare at my feet. Endless peaks and valleys stretched out below. I imagined this was how Neal Armstrong felt when he stood on the surface of the moon and gazed down at that pale blue dot.

"What do you think, brother?" T hovered just behind my left shoulder.

"I'm not sure," I said. "I think a lot of things. I feel a lot of things."

"Well," T said. "Look around! Do you think you see salvation waiting for you here at the top of this old rock?"

"Maybe." I smiled. I let the moment envelop me. I saw those miserable nights in Florida growing ever further away. At the same time, the golden days of youth were travelling in the same direction just as fast. For just an instant, the doors of my own perception were cleansed by the grace of Grandfather, and I saw the universe for what it is: infinite. I existed only in that moment, as did everything else that ever had or would happen. I felt—for just a split second—true and complete mindfulness, as all of my life spilled out before me, and all that was left was me and my thoughts. "Wow."

"It's not the same as before, is it?" T asked. He indicated towards the landscape stretching below us. "It's different, now."

"It's more beautiful than ever."

"Isn't it wonderful when things get better with time?"

"It is," I said. "You think some things will never change. And then, ten years later... they haven't. But they're still different. Maybe I'm different. I remember every peak and valley that I can see, but they aren't the same." I shook my head. "Am I making any sense?"

"Does it make sense to you?"

"Well, the idea does," I said, and then laughed. "Dunno about the words, though."

"Sometimes, you don't need words. I know just what you mean." He paused. "I think, maybe, that everything is exactly as it was. But it looks different to you, because you're different."

"Maybe," I said. "I mean, of course I'm different. I feel like it's been a whole lifetime since the last time we tried to make this climb."

"It has, my friend."

"C'mon, T. You know what I mean. It's only been ten years."

"And how much has changed in ten years?"

I didn't respond, at first. I finished my cigarette, slowly relishing each puff. I strained my eyes, looking out as far as I could see. I tried to remember everything that had happened in the last ten years. My reverie was broken by the sound of T's voice.

"If you're not going to answer that, let's try a different question."

"Okay," I said. "What've you got, T?"

"You said you were different, right? I mean, different from last time."

"Yeah... What're you getting at?"

"Are you better, or worse?"

"T," I said. "That's a pretty tough question. I don't even know what you mean by that."

"Brother!" His voice was hauntingly jubilant. "You're standing at the top of the world! This is all you ever wanted, right? This was what you needed? So look back. Look back ten years ago. Look back to last year in Florida. Look back to the day you parked your car at the trailhead. Now, we all know you're not perfect—and you never will be. But right now, standing up here. Are you better?"

"T." A tear rolled down my cheek. "I... I am better. But I shouldn't be. I don't deserve to be."

"Cut that bull, my brother." T's smile was wider than any valley below us. "I think it was you who once told me, 'things have a way of working themselves out.' And here you are, after everything, making the dream come true."

I fought back the tears. "It wasn't supposed to happen like this, though, brother."

"Let it go." His voice was serene. "You're here now. And you are better than you were. You're better than a year ago, and you're better than three days ago. I know it, and you know it."

I nodded. "T, there's something I have to do."

"I know," he said. "You haven't finished what you planned for this trip. Go ahead, it's time."

"Are you sure, T?" The tears were streaking down my face. "Maybe we should sit for another hour, and soak up the sun. Enjoy a talk. There's no rush, right?"

"It's time," he said.
I nodded and walked slowly back towards my pack.

Leaving the Ranch 38

I gave everyone one last hug just as my cab pulled through the gate. Margot smiled at me and waved as I climbed inside. It felt like a cheesy movie scene as I pulled away, returning the waves out the back window at her and all of my assembled group of friends. They gave me a proper send-off, their arms flailing furiously in the air as they shouted words of encouragement. I was smiling when the gate closed behind me.

For the first few minutes, we rode in silence. I flipped through my phone, happy to have it back again after a month without it. I scrolled through a sea of missed calls and messages. Slowly and methodically, I deleted the numbers of everyone who wouldn't be a part of my new life going forward. Then, referencing a ripped sheet of notebook paper, I added the numbers of all the new friends I had made locked away in the alternate reality of The Ranch. Last of all, I pulled out the paper tucked deep inside me pocket. Smiling, I typed Margot's number into my phone and pushed save.

The cab driver suddenly spoke up. "Looks like they gave you a hell of a send off, huh, guy?"

"Yeah," I said. "They did." My face was beaming. The outpouring of love and support from a group of people who had been strangers a month ago touched me far more deeply than I ever could have dreamed of. I felt free. But more than that, I felt determined. As the Texas Hill Country flashed by the window, all I could see was the mountains of North Carolina. I could see the face of Grandfather, watching and waiting.

"Seemed like nice people," the driver said. "Not what you'd expect to see at a place like this, ya' know?"

A month earlier, I might've been offended. Instead, I simply shook my head. "Nice people and lousy people, we all go through hard times. It doesn't take a bad person to make bad decisions."

"Ah, I'm sorry, guy." He looked back at me, just for a moment. "I didn't mean anything by it. My mom, ya' know, she had to go to a place like this. There's just a certain image in your head, ya' know?"

"Of course," I said. "I told you, I'm not offended. I thought the same way. I figured that I was different, and the people I'd see there wouldn't be like me. But they were. They were a lot of good people who hit some hard times. They all had stories just like I did." I paused. "Like I do. Because the story never ends, right?"

"Sure, sure." He sped up a little. I could tell he felt like he said something he shouldn't have.

"I'm not offended," I reiterated. "So, really, don't worry about it. I appreciate you driving all the way the hell out here to pick me up and not charging me something crazy for it."

"Like I said," he replied. "My mom was at a place like this. I try not to judge. I guess we all do sometimes, though... but I feel lousy about saying that."

"Don't worry about it." I was still staring at the window. I was lost in visions of Grandfather. I remembered T's smile, how it stretched so wide across his face that his happiness practically radiated out into the world around. I thought about the way that smile would look when I stood on top of the peak and made right all the wrongs of the world.

"So, ya' goin' home now, or what?"

"Not really," I said. "I'm gonna stop through San Antonio for a bit, but after that I'm going out east. I'm gonna head up to North Carolina and climb a mountain."

"Climb a mountain?" I could hear the mixture of disbelief and confusion in his voice. "Why the hell are ya' gonna take off and climb a mountain?"

"Because," I answered. "There are a lot of things I can't change. But ten years ago, my best friend and I let Grandfather Mountain beat us. After that, for years, I let a lot of things beat me. It's about time I started turning it all around, and stopped accepting failure."

"Yeah, okay." He didn't say anything else, instead he reached down and turned the radio up, just a little. Maybe he thought I was crazy, but it didn't really make any difference at that point.

I looked down at my phone and scrolled through to T's name. I thought about calling, just for the hell of it. But there was no need. It had already been decided. I would find him at the same trailhead that we'd found a decade earlier, and together we would conquer the mountain. Together, we would find a way to make everything okay again.

39

The world felt surreal as I stepped slowly towards my pack. I was consumed by a joyous sadness. I rooted through my possessions. I stared at each item, and then gently set them aside on the ground next to the pack. Finally, I came to the very bottom, and to the only two items left that mattered.

First, I pulled out the scotch. I examined the bottle. I read every tiny bit of print on the label. Eventually, I opened it. I wafted the air above the bottle towards my face and breathed deeply. Faintly, in the back of my throat, I could already taste the bittersweet burning of victory. I closed the bottle and set it down next to me.

Last of all, I pulled out the small, ornate wooden box that was hidden in the very farthest reaches of my pack. For a moment, I pulled it tightly to my chest. I held my breath and closed my eyes. I tried, with every fiber of my being, to push the sadness from my heart and appreciate the moment for what it was. I searched for joy and found it, in the sound of T's voice floating in the wind. "It's time, brother. I'm ready. I know you're ready, too."

"Yeah, T," I said to myself, in a voice so low that I thought only I could hear it.

"Come on," he answered. "It's time."

I stood up and headed towards the peak. The bottle of scotch was in my left hand, and the box was clutched tightly in my right. At the very furthest point, I sat down on an outcropping of rock, letting my feet dangle above the endless space below. "One last cigarette, okay?"

"Whatever you have to do, my brother." He sounded older than he ever had. Even in the simplest of his words, there was some ancient wisdom.

"I'm glad we got to do this, T. I really am." Tears were already welling up in the corners of my eyes. I tried to puff as lightly as possible. I wanted that cigarette to last forever. I could feel his presence behind me—all around me.

I flicked the cigarette butt over the edge of the cliff. Caught in a wind draft, it floated high into the air, disappearing like a phantom into the distance. For just a moment, I set the box down. T was next to me, now, standing tall in the glistening light.

"Is that it, T? Did we find peace?"

"I did," he answered. "I don't suffer, not anymore. Maybe you'll still suffer a little, yet, but not like before. You'll find your peace. I know it."

"You wouldn't lie to me, T?"

"I wouldn't." I knew, above me, he was smiling. It would be the same big, wide smile as always.

"I trust you." I opened the bottle of scotch and stood up. I took one last breath of the delicious aroma and brought the bottle up to my lips. It tasted like freedom. It tasted like salvation. It tasted like peace. Even as that small sip of liquid was running down my throat, I reached the bottle outwards. I began to turn the bottle, deliberately, an inch at a time, until it was upside down. The golden trophy of my achievement flowed down the mountainside. I watched, in silence, until every last drop was gone.

I turned my eyes, next, upon the box. I felt its weight. One last time, I turned it upside down and traced the words carved into the bottom. In elegant, golden script was carved T's name. The tears flowed freely as I opened the box. I held it high, letting its contents drift into the wind. His ashes scattered out, fluttering across Grandfather's face and into the void. Each particle caught the rays of the sun, glittering brilliantly until they vanished against the horizon. With one last shining burst of light, it was all gone. The ashes disappeared, as everything does.

Behind me, the visage of T faded away. He didn't speak or cry out. He just slowly disappeared, until there was nothing left but the sun and the wind and trees. I sat alone at the top of the world, bathed in my own tears, and holding two empty mementos of the best man I'd ever known. I spoke into the wind, letting the sound of my shaking voice carry across the world. "I love you, T. Rest in peace."

40

I'm not sure how long I sat there for, alone at the top of the world. I'm pretty sure that I dangled my legs over the edge of that cliff for what seemed like years. Eventually, the thoughts in my head faded into the background and I was able to relax. I tried to appreciate the glory of my victory. As minutes passed, all the mistakes I'd made floated into the wind, one by one.

It was then that I realized the enormity of it all. I'd trekked up the side of a mountain, alone, seeking salvation, and here, at the top, the world was still the same. "What would you think of it all, T?"

The ghosts in the breeze gave no answer. I heard only the rustling of leaves and the soft chirping of birds. The endless universe would offer me no knowledge that I wasn't already privy to. Eventually, I pulled myself away from the cliffside and stumbled back towards my pack. I carefully tucked away the box and the bottle...both now empty. I stared off into the distance.

"I hope you're out there, brother." I shook my head. "Here I am, again, talking to myself. I guess that's just how it is now. I wish I believed that you were up there smiling down on me. Hell, I don't know what I believe half the time. I wish I knew if this whole thing was for you or for me. But, I guess I'm here and you're not, so the end result is the same, right?"

The mountain offered only silence in return. Grandfather didn't speak. The wind blew just the same as it had moments before. The leaves rustled the same, and the branches swayed all the same. The mountain was unchanged. In that moment, though, if only for a brief instant, I was changed.

Without thinking, I opened my mouth and shouted at the top of my lungs. "I made it! I made it, and everything you tried to do to stop me didn't mean a damn thing! I made it. We made it." And then, echoing in the back of my head, I could hear a familiar voice. "Things have a way of working themselves out, right?"

"Yeah," I said to the wide empty world. "They do, T." A pause. "Journey to the end, right, T? I let you down once, T. And you died. But I am here, and I'll go on. Your spirit and memories will always be with me, and I will conquer myself and whatever challenges I don't even know about yet." I felt the tears coming again, and made no effort to fight them. There's no shame in crying when the only witness is an ancient rock face. I wanted to think I'd reached the end of my journey, but I knew there would be more. On the mountaintop, I was a conqueror. In the world below, I was just another man clawing his way up, refusing to believe that he could be broken.

Truth be told, I had no idea how I was supposed to feel. This climb had been my entire world for six months. The planning, the plotting, and the final simple action of forcing my battered body up into the clouds. I wasn't sure what to do or where to go. So I stood there, at Attic Window with wandering thoughts.

A faint noise reached my ears, coming from the bottom of my pack. It was a buzzing sound, just barely audible. I reached down into the bag and pulled out a small pay-by-the-minute flip-phone that I had all but forgotten about, concealed just in case of the most extreme of emergencies. I'd missed ten calls, all from the same number. I didn't recognize it. The phone rang again. With some trepidation, I answered.

"Yeah?"

"I thought you were dead! Where the hell have you been?"

My face lit up. Ignoring the static and poor reception, I was thrilled to hear the voice on the other end. "M!"

"Everyone's been looking for you. What happened? Are you hurt?" I couldn't tell if she was happy or furious. Most likely, it was a mix of both.

"M," I said. "I did it. I climbed the mountain."

There was a pause. "The one from before?"

"Yeah ... Grandfather. I guess when I got to the top my emergency phone finally caught a signal. I'm standing here right now."

"So you did it? You should've told someone where you were going. We've been looking for you for days. Your whole family thought you were dead."

"More alive than I've ever been,Margot. I had to do this. You know I had to do this." I breathed a deep sigh of relief. "But, it is good to hear a real, live voice again."

"Well," she said. "It's a relief to hear from you. But disappearing like this... Are you okay?"

"I'm..." I paused, and wiped the last tear from my eye. I felt the sun on my back and tasted the mountain air. I gazed at the face of Grandfather, staring back across the chasm. I turned my gaze from the abyss and smiled at the beauty of the world around me.

"Yeah, I AM okay."

Made in the USA
Columbia, SC
08 August 2021